NEANDERTAL MAN

CRO-MAGNON MAN

tesy of Dr. J. H. McGregor

MAN'S FIRST MILLION YEARS

with W. Maxwell Reed

ANIMALS ON THE MARCH

MAN'S FIRST MILLION YEARS

by *JANNETTE M. LUCAS*

ILLUSTRATED BY JAMES MAC DONALD

HARCOURT, BRACE AND COMPANY
NEW YORK

This book is dedicated

to

NELS C. NELSON

who has forgotten more than I shall ever know.

Dedicating this book to Dr. Nelson is only a slight return for his long and kindly interest. Without him I do not think the book would have been completed, but it must be understood that any errors are my own, undoubtedly made in those unhappy moments when I was separated from his generous help.

I actually got the idea for these pages some years ago when I discovered that I had worked for some days on a scientific bibliography without realizing that the men spoken of by one set of authors and the cultures written about by a different group were not only contemporary but that the cultures were the work of the "fossils," one described by paleontologists, the other by anthropologists. Since then I have tried to help both writers and artists find material so that their work might be accurate. The search impressed upon me my need for a simple statement of the general field. In correlating a number of sources I wrote this book.

J. M. L.

TABLE OF CONTENTS

1. WHEN MAN BEGAN   3

2. MAN'S EARLY ANCESTORS   9

3. THE RECORDS OF THE EARLIEST ANCESTORS   22

4. WHERE MAN FIRST APPEARED   34

5. THE APE-MAN OF JAVA—THE FIRST MAN   38

6. PEKING MAN—THE FIRST MAN IN CHINA   52

7. BETWEEN MEN   66

8. THE PILTDOWN MAN OF ENGLAND   75

9. PRE-CHELLEAN AND CHELLEAN INTERLUDE   90

10. HEIDELBERG MAN—CHELLEAN?   112

11. NEANDERTAL MAN—DENIZEN OF THE WORLD   118

12. NEANDERTAL MAN—ACHEULIAN AND MOUSTERIAN CULTURES   131

13. MANNERS AND CUSTOMS OF THE NEANDERTALS   146

14. THE GRIMALDI RACE—STRANGERS IN EUROPE   154

15. THE CRO-MAGNONS, INVADERS WITH IDEAS   161

16. THE ART OF THE AURIGNACIANS   181

17. SOLUTREANS—FLINT WORKERS AND STONE AGE IMMIGRANTS   195

18. THE LAST STAND OF UNPOLISHED STONE   207

19. ADVANCING TIME AND CHANGED CULTURES   225

20. A CHANGING WORLD   238

21. CATCHING UP WITH THE CONTINENTS   252

BIBLIOGRAPHY   269

INDEX   273

MAN'S FIRST MILLION YEARS

1

WHEN MAN BEGAN

THE earth was old when man came to it. For nearly two thousand million years the continents had changed and changed again. Great races of animals had come into existence only to vanish completely from the shifting scenes. An even longer time must have passed before any life at all existed on the earth.

This incredibly long span of time before history began has been divided into periods by the geologists who are the earth's historians. These periods are of varying length but the duration of each is estimated in millions of years. Usually each period has some special geologic event—such as the rise of a mountain chain or the formation of coal-fields —as its peculiar characteristic. As these periods approach our own time they grow shorter. The

Pliocene, last but one in the chain of periods, lasted six million years and the last period is the shortest of all.

This is called the Pleistocene and is only one million years in length. Those million years saw the last great geologic event, the advance and retreat of glaciers over nearly the entire world. For this reason this period is sometimes spoken of as the Great Ice Age. One other event of supreme importance took place during Pleistocene time. That strangest of all animals—man—appeared. During this time man endured terrors he could not understand, survived hardships almost as difficult as polar travel, faced the loss of his food supply when plants perished and animals fled before moving walls of ice.

The Pleistocene forms the last of the periods in what may be called Ancient Time. Ancient Time has no written history. The geologists read its record in the continents and the rocks, the materials of which they are made, and in the waters which surround them. On these studies they can,

4

with much accuracy, re-create the vanished periods of Ancient Time.

In this they have the help of the paleontologists who study the fossils made during all the periods of the past. A fossil was once a living creature the hard parts of whose body have been transformed into rock. Soft parts decay. It is just possible that when most of the soft parts have decayed an exceptionally dry air will mummify the tougher tendons and skin until the entire mummy is ready to be turned into a fossil. You must have mud to make a fossil. Water, seeping through the earth, carries various substances dissolved in its drops. These penetrate the bones, washing away the animal matter and taking its place until at last the entire bone has been turned to stone. Sometimes the mud in which the bone rested is plunged deep into the earth by an earthquake. Sometimes tons of sand or earth are blown over both mud and bone. Then they slowly turn to rock together and you have a stone within a stone or, as the paleontologist says, a fossil in its matrix. Many of these fossils must be quarried out of the earth or dug from some distance below the surface. Their name comes from this—from the Latin *foedere*—to dig. Sometimes some vast, distant catastrophe has heaved the fossil to the surface again—into a world completely different from that which once saw the fossil as a living creature.

Man's first records are fossils, and as the paleontologist helps the geologist he in turn receives aid. This he gets from anatomists, who study living forms and so write their histories of man not in terms of rock and bone but in terms of bone, muscle, flesh, and brain. They help the paleontologist re-create the form from the bones—the living creature from his fossilized record.

Pleistocene means most recent, and the name means that it was the most recent of the periods of Ancient Time. Some thirty or forty thousand years have passed since the Pleistocene ended. This period is called Recent Time. To the geologist Recent Time means not modern time but that period when the earth had assumed its present conditions and

6

when most of the animals could be recognized as easily as living ones are now. We live in Recent Time but we also live in the smallest subdivision of time—Historic Time. Historic Time is that part of Recent Time when man has used his self-taught skill to record his own actions in writing.

The historian's work lies within the limit of Historic Time but he is steadily pushing that limit into the region of Recent Time which was once supposed to belong to the geologist alone. In his work of studying man's actions as a series of connected events the historian receives help from students of various arts and from the archaeologist. All these men study the records man has left of himself—his tools, weapons, ornaments, pottery, sculpture, painting, and architecture.

By combining all these careful and minute studies, the life work of many men which fills millions and millions of printed pages, and by accepting the main facts without writing out the full proof which science demands we can make the briefest sketch of man. This story begins just a little before it can be said—"Well, it doesn't look *quite* right but it is a man certainly." It ends at a point when man began to express his ideas about himself. It is the story of man's first million years.

2

MAN'S EARLY ANCESTORS

THE history of man really begins with the history of his ancestors and, since the records of these ancestors are their fossilized bones, this part of the history is largely the work of the paleontologist and the anatomist. To both these men a bone is much more than a bone. It is more than the record of the individual to whom it once belonged. By comparing one bone with a similar bone from an individual of different kind or period changes are often revealed. Checked by innumerable comparisons these changes may trace the history of a race.

The same is true of other parts of the body. To the history written in bone, read by both himself and the paleontologist, the anatomist adds his special version. Part of this he does by noting the slow change made by some organ of the body. For instance there is our famous appendix. This is a relic of millions of years ago when the digestive arrangements of some far distant ancestor demanded very different intestines. It has outlived its usefulness as it all too often testifies and it has become what the anatomist tactfully calls a "vestigial organ"—the left-behind record of another way of life.

That is one example. Teeth, which paleontologists and zoologists (students of living animals) study carefully when deciding an animal's identity and relationships, have had an enormously long history of their own. From crude teeth set like thorns on the cartilage jaws of shark-like ancestors living hundreds of millions of years ago teeth have changed until they have finally become as they are today.

The very face man shows the world tells a history of progress "from fish to man," as one scientist has said. Very little needs to be filled in and this supplied material is based on one fact and connects with another. In such ways is told the history of man's early ancestors.

These ancestors were not human nor were they such apes as we have today—orangs, gorillas, chimpanzees, or gibbons. It has been fashionable to call them pre-human. Well, they were. They were very far from human. Although no self-respecting ape today would recognize them, they were certainly ape-like creatures. The ancestor from which man sprang must have separated himself from the ape-group very, very far in the past indeed. At first it was thought that this might have happened about thirty million years ago but now we are inclined to believe that it was very much earlier than that. Geologist, paleontologist, and anatomist, all working together, may even thrust that first ancestor farther away; they will not bring him nearer to our time.

Such a distant ancestor may have been a creature like *Notharctus*. This animal lived in the land which, forty million years ago, extended where North America now lies. Many of *Notharctus'* contemporaries were the ancestors of living animals. That is why the age is called Dawn of the Recent, but it takes a paleontologist and an anatomist to recognize the ancestors.

Notharctus and its kin were tree-dwellers and remained tree-dwellers for many millions of years. They had good eyesight since they had to judge distances and recognize friends and foes through thick leaves. They were agile as befitted creatures whose every road bent and swayed with each movement. They didn't think a great deal and their thoughts were centered about the next meal. Since they owned very capable teeth this probably consisted of leaves, soft bark, roots, berries, fruits, grubs, insects, eggs, and fledglings. In short, they had the beginning of a fine omnivorous appetite— one which makes everything taste good.

After some millions of years finding a good meal took more thought because it was growing more difficult to find food. The land had changed and so the climate had altered and the trees and plants were changing with the changing winds. After a

"NOTHARCTUS," DISTANT ANCESTOR OF THE HU-
MAN RACE, LIVED IN NORTH AMERICA FORTY MIL-
LION YEARS AGO.

while some of the tree-dwellers were forced to hunt food on the ground. Not all of them. Many were determined not to give up a way of living which they liked. They were, probably, quite ready to thrust any less determined animal out into a new life and insist that the earth was a splendid place— for others. As hard times increased, more and more inhabitants came to earth, pushed along the road to manhood by their conservative relatives. Of course this did not happen quickly; it took count- less thousands of years.

At first there may have been a sort of daily picnic on the ground with a return to the tree-shelters in the dusk. Then, as they used it more and more, the earth became commonplace and some grew so used to it that they decided it was a nuisance to climb back and live in the trees. The young, born and reared on the ground, found trees difficult for daily use. After a while one group lived on the ground entirely—only taking to the trees in case of danger. So after thousands of years there was a tree-group and a ground-group, and when pressure

15

above produced new immigrants those below thrust them farther and farther into the wilderness.

Now the types of hands and feet which help in trees aren't as useful on the ground. Feet particularly are quite different. Gradually the feet changed to bear the weight of an upright body walking on a flat, steady surface instead of clinging to swaying, curved branches. Walking erect left the hands free to grasp things and a change came about in them also. Man depends a great deal on being able to make his thumb meet any of his fingers or stand away from them. This is the "opposable thumb." Some of the apes possess this ability but very rarely make use of it. Their thumbs are much shorter in proportion than man's thumb and the skin runs farther toward the second joint than the skin on man's hand. To apes hands are climbing members; to man they are grasping members. Somewhere along the long road of the ages man's ancestors developed the great skill and movement of this small digit.

The use of the thumb is controlled by the part of

16

the brain which had already been exercised by the use of the eyes. In these ancestor's ancestors the case which held the brain was of heavy bone. The bone was heavy because the muscles attached to it were themselves heavy and needed strong bone for

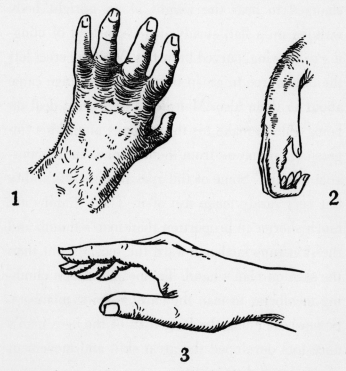

THUMB OF APE COMPARED WITH THUMB OF MAN.

1. GORILLA   2. ORANGOUTANG   3. MAN

17

anchorage. The muscles were heavy for two reasons. Those at the back of the neck had to hold the head suspended at an angle from the spine. The muscles of the jaws, which are anchored toward the crown of the head, were heavy so that they could put power into the bite of teeth in a out-thrust jaw.

As the backbone grew straighter and the eyes grew used to looking over leaves instead of through them, the head moved upward and backward until it rested on the top of the backbone. This did not make such a strain on the muscles and less heavy ones were needed. Lighter muscles could be fastened on lighter bone.

So as the head moved upright on the neck the very shape of it changed and the part of the brain which controlled sight, smell, and the grasping powers of the hands got more room to fill in its thinner bone-box. In the heads of babies of both apes and men today these bones stay soft a long time and it was so, in all probability, in those far-off times. The ancestral babies got a chance to walk

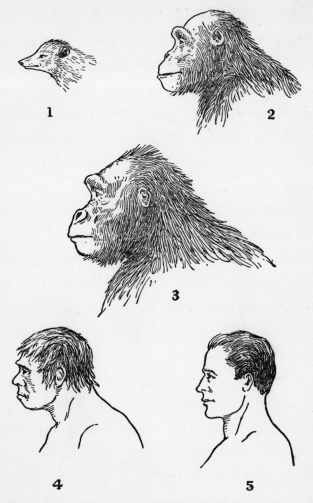

THE POSITION OF THE HEAD ON THE BODY. NOTE
HOW THE HEAD STRAIGHTENS UP.

1. OPOSSUM   3. GORILLA   4. NEANDERTAL MAN

2. CHIMPANZEE   5. MAN TODAY

erect before these bones hardened. Consequently they could develop and use larger brains before the space to be occupied was permanently fixed. After millions of years the descendants of the ground-dwellers had more brains and better used brains than the descendants of the tree-dwellers.

3

THE RECORDS OF THE
EARLIEST ANCESTORS

ALTHOUGH man has no fully connected series of fossils to show the steady progress of his development, there are a number of individual specimens each of which shows one phase of evolution. These come from rocks which belong to periods between the age of *Notharctus* and the age of man, the Pleistocene.

All serve to show that apes and man have much in common and to prove Linnaeus right. In 1758 this Swedish naturalist successfully accomplished his self-imposed task of arranging all living creatures, so far as he knew them, in orderly groups. Linnaeus made a monkey-ape-man group which he called *primates* or first animals. First meant most important. Primates have large brain-boxes containing well-developed brains, fore-limbs adapted for grasping with hands having flat nails, and teeth capable of chewing a mixed diet. Linnaeus' Latin description for man was *Homo sapiens*—man of thought, or better, capable of thought.

Among the primates which were the earliest relatives of man is one called *Propliopithecus*. This monkey lived in Africa over thirty million years ago in the region now known as the Fayum. Now that is a desert but at that far away time there was a large lake there and lakes have, in warm countries at least, tropical vegetation about them with a great deal of good eating in tender twigs, leaves, fruits, and bird's eggs. *Propliopithecus* probably lived much as monkeys do today but we really know very little about him for all the fossils ever found are two lower jaws. The teeth in these jaws are very important for they leave no doubt about their owner's relationships. He was ancestral to an ape found at a later geological time in Europe and also to man. *Pro* means before, so the whole name means that he was the ancestor of another ape

23

called *Pliopithecus*. This scientific name, as well as others we shall use, does not refer to a single animal but to a group of the same species.

Pliopithecus, the Ancient Pliocene Ape, was found a century ago in deposits about ten million years more recent than those holding his ancestor. This time the discovery was made in France and it too was a single lower jaw. Since then other bones have been found in other parts of Europe and we have a little more idea about the Ancient Pliocene Ape's appearance. The really important thing about the first jawbone, however, was its tooth-pattern. Tooth-pattern is a great deal more than the arrangement of teeth in a jaw. It involves the arrangement of the humps and hollows—as they seem to us—in the teeth themselves. The scientist who studies teeth knows that these arrangements alter as animals progress in time but retain enough likeness to older patterns so that they may be trusted as a genealogical tree. *Pliopithecus'* tooth-pattern not only shows that *Propliopithecus* was his ancestor but that he, himself, was an ancestor to

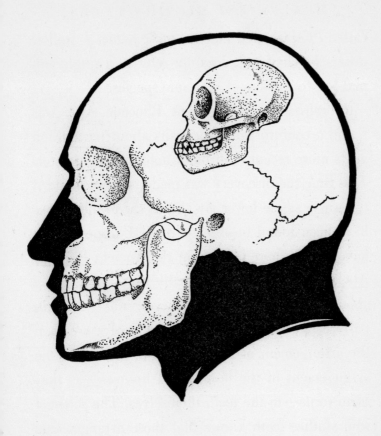

THE SMALL SKULL IS THAT OF "PROPLIOPITHE-
CUS," A REMOTE ANCESTOR OF MAN WHO LIVED
MILLIONS OF YEARS AGO. SHOWING THE COMPARA-
TIVE SIZE TO SKULL OF MODERN MAN.

living gibbons and to man.

Then there was *Dryopithecus*. He began his existence at the time of *Pliopithecus* but his race extended several million years later; that is, *Dryopithecus* apes were living after the *Pliopithecus* apes were dead. At first fossils were found in Europe but within the last few years many more have been found in India. So we realize that *Dryopithecus* was a member of a great ape race spread over both Europe and Asia for millions of years. He was about the size of a chimpanzee and undoubtedly— his fossils say—lived in trees. Like his earlier relatives the greatest interest of *Dryopithecus* lies in what his teeth reveal to scientists. Besides the pattern of his molar teeth, which show that he must have stood in a line from which both apes and man separated, *Dryopithecus* has much smaller canines (dog-teeth) than the other fossil primates. Since living man has very small canines indeed and since fossil man changed as he neared modern time, this is an important fact.

Another fossil ape created a great deal of excitement when it was found in 1913. This was found in Bechuanaland and was given a very long name—the Ape of the African Part of the Southern World. Unfortunately the first discovery was a young individual and fossils as well as humans must be fully grown before we can be *sure* just what they are really like. Fortunately an incomplete skull of an adult was found later which left no doubt that this was the most man-like of fossil apes. It clearly shows that the gap between apes and man is one which may some day be completely filled by a series of fossils.

Much time has been spent in the study of teeth of apes and men and it is this work, the most important part of which has been done in America, which makes it possible to talk about tooth-patterns and their meaning. All that has been written would fill many volumes but a true story illustrates how much alike the teeth of apes and men really are.

A scientist whom we'll call Dr. Jones went to consult another scientist, Dr. Smith. Smith was not in his office so Jones left a little box and a note

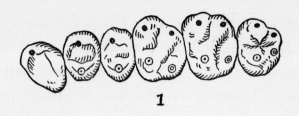

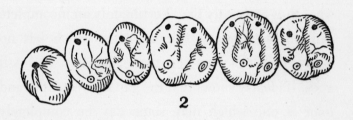

TEETH—RELATIONSHIP BETWEEN MAN AND APE.

1. MAN   2. MOUSTERIAN MAN   3. APE

Courtesy of Dr. Gregory and the American Museum of Natural History

on his desk. The note said in scientific language: "This is a tooth which has just come from the west. It is Pliocene and is supposed to be an ape's. Will you give me your opinion?"

This was very important because, if true, it would put apes in a completely new place and earlier time than any found before in the west.

As Dr. Smith worked on the tooth he grew more and more puzzled for he did *not* think the tooth Pliocene or that of an ape. He compared the new fossil with fossil teeth or with careful casts of fossil teeth. Then he compared it with human teeth; and at last he made up his mind.

"This tooth," said Dr. Smith, "is the milk molar of a young child."

Dr. Jones gave a shout and began to hunt frantically in his pockets. For this is what had happened: That morning while he had been examining the new fossil and writing a report on it, his pen had hit something hard in the ink-well. Investigation had disclosed that his youngest daughter had thought the ink-well a good place to hide her recently lost tooth.

He put the tooth on a blotter and went on with his work. When, later on, he packed up the fossil tooth to take it to Dr. Smith, he substituted the child's tooth for the fossil by mistake. But the real fossil was safe and in the end it turned out not to be an ape's either but a much worn tooth of a quite different animal.

The point is that Dr. Smith, who knew perhaps more about teeth than any other scientist, realized that apes' teeth and men's teeth are so much alike that he spent hours of work before he was sure exactly what the specimen was.

All the relationships of early primates, both apes and men, have been most carefully studied. All that bones and teeth can be made to tell has been told. Few fossils have been discovered, so each one is probably studied more carefully than if thousands were available. Each piece has been made to yield every possible bit of information.

But how can we expect many bits of fossil evidence? All primate bones are rather fragile and even after they left the trees these ancestors of ancestors lived in or near forests. Creatures that live in forests die in forests too. On the leafy, moist floor their outworn bodies slowly fall to pieces. While bones outlast decaying flesh, they too rot in time and leave no trace.

Only the unwary creature caught, perhaps, at some water hole falls into preserving mud. Or it may be that an inundated forest has preserved in its muddy debris the body of another exhausted forest-dweller. From such scant material have come our clues to the mystery of man.

So, though the Missing Link has not been found, though we cannot put the history of man into a museum case as we can the history of the horse, we *can* put together many bits of evidence. We can be sure that we have traced not only the story of our ancestors but of our ancestors' ancestors.

4

WHERE MAN FIRST APPEARED

WE can only guess at man's birthplace. Of course it is not the kind of a guess you and I make when we shut our eyes, jab a pencil at a map and say, "Here!" What a scientist calls guessing means putting together all the facts he can find and drawing a conclusion which, while it fits the known facts, cannot be proved by actual evidence. It is so that Asia has been chosen as the birthplace of man and the guess goes something like this:

Man developed from some ape-like stock which he and other primates shared in common.

All lands where animals have improved for thousands of years have been lands with mild climates, various kinds of country, and enough but not too much food.

34

At a point in Ancient Time, a few million years before man appeared, there was a vast plateau in Asia north of the present Himalayas. The climate there was not cold nor was it tropical. No animal would have wished to sleep all the time when not eating. He would have wished to explore new country because he needed to ⬛ around and food was not immediately under his hands. On this plateau there were forests, plains, and open land. Some of these places had plenty of rain; others were deserts—for the plateau was vast. Not many of the plants were good to eat but there was plenty of game. Any living creature in this region could have been comfortable in a sort of camping life, if he had hunted for the comfort.

There were primates in Asia before the earliest records of man. Those primates differed both from living primates and from man, but could have developed into either or both.

The first of the human creatures was found in Asia and the greatest number of possible ancestral forms were also there. Asia seems a probable homeland for humanity. So we sometimes say that the Himalayas (which are part of this old plateau) were the cradle of the human race.

There is some dispute over this statement however. No one says that man might not have developed in just such a country. Everyone agrees that he could have done so. Some scientists think that the same conditions in other continents might have developed man in those lands. Some speak of Africa. Conditions were much the same there in Ancient Time. The most man-like apes live there today, and the most man-like fossil ape, the Ape of the African Part of the Southern World, has been found on that continent. This ape cannot be considered as an ancestor of man, however, since he lived at too late a date. But he could have diverged from some common ancestor.

We shall have to wait for the discovery of more fossil bones and the paleontologist's study of them before we can know positively which continent was the birthplace of the human race. Actual evidence of only a few hundreds of the millions of apes

36

which must have lived on the various continents of Ancient Time has been found. The very earliest men were probably dwellers on the floors of forests, for to them the trees must have served as shelters. Those who ventured on the plains were always alert to avoid the floods and sand-storms which caught and preserved so many animals. Ability to escape provided future generations but no evidence of the past. Only those creatures, slower of thought and action, who perished disastrously were preserved for posterity.

These early members of the Man Family were not like the "type" of the family, for the type is *Homo sapiens*, Thinking Man, as we know him today—a dominant creature not content with thoughts but endeavoring to readjust the entire world to his various ideas. *Homo sapiens* was several hundreds of thousands of years in developing, but the earliest member of the Man Family we know was more like living man than like any other primate.

5

THE APE-MAN OF JAVA—
THE FIRST MAN

THIS first creature to be identified as human was found in Java, an island off southern Asia belonging to the Dutch. Eugene Dubois who discovered it was a Dutch army surgeon who had been fossil hunting for many years in the hope that he might discover the fabled "Missing Link." Until 1891 he had no success. Then, near Trinil, he found a single upper molar tooth which he thought belonged to a new species of ape. At least it had certainly belonged to a primate. Very carefully he cleared away the rock in which the tooth had been found. About three feet deeper was the top of a skull. Then the rains of a tropical country began and further work was impossible. When the rains ceased, Dubois resumed

38

his search and some fifty feet from the first tooth he found a second and a thigh-bone.

That thigh-bone settled the matter. He might doubt the humanness of the skull and teeth but he could not doubt the thigh-bone. Dubois was an anatomist as all surgeons must be and he knew that no ape had owned the leg of which this bone had been a part. For the owner of that leg had walked erect! Only muscles working in an erect posture could have been attached to such a bone.

Dubois hesitated no longer. In 1894 he described his various finds, and called the ancient human ancestor whose bones he had found the Ape-man who Walked Erect. He is now often referred to as the Ape-man of Java.

The rest of this Ape-man was not nearly so imposing as his ability to stand upright. His eyes were sunk deep under enormous brows formed by a bony projection which made a ridge across the entire skull. The forehead sloped backward from these brows in a very ape-like manner.

For a good many years this was all that was

39

known about the Ape-man of Java. Dubois retained possession of the bones and refused to allow any further study of them to be made. But finally scientists interested in the brain of man succeeded in securing permission to have the skull freed from the matrix (the rock in which it had been found) which filled the interior. A cast was made which was a plaster model of the Ape-man of Java's brain made from the inside of his own skull. While it does not show the exact shape of the brain surface, it is close to it. The cast showed the brain capacity to be larger than any ape's but less than that of any living man.

Further study showed that the Ape-man of Java was probably human beyond doubt. It revealed, at least to one group of scientists, that he must have been able to utter and understand a limited number of sounds. No ape had ever achieved this. Although his vocabulary was certainly very limited, he could speak.

Just a few years after this amazing discovery another skull was found. In 1936 the skull of a

THE APE-MAN OF JAVA.

Courtesy of Dr. J. H. McGregor

child was discovered in Java. It is the skull of a child not more than four years old and it is very different from the skulls of modern children of that age. The bone ridges across the forehead are heavier than those of any skull of primitive man so far found. The forehead recedes more than that of any other skull in spite of the fact that the forehead of so young a child is more nearly upright than it is at any later age. Now it has been proved that the child belonged to the same race as the previously discovered Ape-man of Java. Fragments of skulls, jaws, and teeth have been found in other parts of Java. All these have added to our knowledge until the place of the Ape-man of Java as a leading pre-hominid—a man in the process of development—has been established.

One skull, found in 1937, probably belonged to a woman. To the scientist a man's skull and a woman's usually look quite different. The greatest difference is at the base of the skull where the muscles which hold it to the neck are fastened. Men have stronger muscles than women and the

43

bones to which they fasten are rougher.

The fossil animals which had been found in the same region gave a chance to speculate about the world in which the Ape-man of Java lived. It must have been very different from the Java of today. For some time scientists differed about the age of the Java Ape-man but it has finally been decided that the animals found in the same strata were Pleistocene. So it is a Pleistocene Java which we must imagine.

In those years Java was not an island. All the islands which stray away from the southern tip of the Malay Peninsula today were then welded together into a huge peninsula stretching into a smaller Pacific Ocean. The ocean was smaller because for thousands of years it had been getting little water to replace that which evaporated. Intense cold was gripping nearly all the world except Asia and the water fell as snow that pressed into ice to cover a freezing continent. In Asia the climate continued rather mild and the great peninsula from which the ocean had retreated was low and tropical. The shores were indented with bays and marshes and the interior had many pools and streams. The trees were such as now grow in the tropics.

There were an amazing number of animals in this country. Some of them are still living there though they have changed with the years. Some have vanished as completely as the Ape-man of Java himself. One of these was an animal which looked rather like a clumsy and heavy giraffe but was no relative. He had hoofs on his hind feet and great claws on his front feet. There was an elephant, looking much like an elephant of today but having very different teeth. There was a huge tapir, as large as a small horse but just like a tapir otherwise. There were great turtles, crocodiles, and one of those strange pangolins which even today look like relics of the past. There were rhinoceroses, hippopotami, buffalo, deer, tigers, and hyenas. Plenty of creatures for any world.

These animals had close relatives living in the Himalayas. It is easy to imagine that they moved

through the low country, browsing here and stray-
ing there as the foraging improved. A few years
would have seen great herds drift through forests
and open country until they reached the long peninsula whose shores stopped further migration.

If such animals as these reached that peninsula,
the ancestors of the Ape-man of Java might have
come in the same way. We can think of small
groups or bands nesting in one place and then in
another spot a few nights later. Probably some
settled permanently at various places along the
route, living in small bands and dying under trees
where their bones were not preserved. Through
thousands of years this slow, irregular march might
have been made north, south, east, and west from
that original high plateau where we have supposed
man's ancestors to have lived.

The Ape-man of Java must have been rather
like his ape-ancestor in appearance and like a
naughty little boy in manner. His skin was probably
dark and hairy and this hair was his only covering.
It was shelter from the sun's rays and from the

THE JAVA APE-MAN LIVED ABOUT ONE MILLION
YEARS AGO.

tropical rain. His little eyes, set under his great brow-ridges, were quick and inquisitive.

He had all the ape's ability to annoy lesser creatures. Like the ape he could lengthen his reach with a stick and many a poor turtle had died on its back because some member of the Ape-man tribe had had fun turning him over to see him squirm. Fledglings were not safe from him and small animals suffered at his hands. He could throw fruit and stones with fair accuracy and even the elephants knew better than to linger in a neighborhood where a group of these half-men disputed existence. Man had already begun his great effort to rid the earth of such animals as he did not find immediately useful.

Of course the Ape-men suffered from some of the animals. The tigers must have killed many of them and the hyenas picked and scattered the bones the tigers left. Crocodiles infested the swimming holes. Many of the tribe must have perished with a choked scream and a swirl of bloody water.

The Java Ape-man probably suffered from his

own nature as well as from the animals. Scientists who make the brain their special study tell us that the cast of his skull shows that he had the quick, gusty temper of most unreasoning creatures. In the swift quarrel of two individuals, disputing over a trifle with snarls and shrieks, the whole tribe must often have been involved. After such a tribal fight many dead bodies must have been left to rot on the jungle floor and beasts of prey must have finished off the wounded.

Torrential rains made life unhappy for long periods of time. Against the down-pour a hairy covering was little good and sodden leaves became impossible beds. Since the Ape-man of Java did not have a brain which could have dealt with fire, he had no cheering flicker to make dripping leaves and wet bark more endurable as he crouched under the great trees.

He had no need of fire for cooking food since he ate everything raw just as his ancestors had done. Yet fire must have been an almost constant source of dread to him. Lightning flashes are awe inspiring even though we have some idea of their cause and action. To a creature who could only see the blinding flash and dread the crash of riven trees, fear must have swooped on almost visible wings.

Equally to be dreaded were earthquakes when the whole earth shook sickeningly under the feet and rivers of destruction poured down the slopes of a mountain throwing flames into a threatening cloud. Then the whole tribe trembled with the shaking earth and, howling with fear, fled for safety—sometimes not fast enough. Of that we have proof.

So the ideal existence we love to picture as part of early, primitive life was never the existence of the Java Ape-man. His joy of life came with the sun which brought warmth and safety.

6

PEKING MAN — THE FIRST MAN IN CHINA

THE human being next in the line of progress is one of the most recently discovered. He also lived in Asia but in the part now known as China.

In 1903 a German paleontologist visiting China found a human tooth among a collection of fossils. These fossils are called "dragon's teeth" in China and Chinese druggists of the old school believe that, when reduced to powder and swallowed, they will cure many ills. Much of the early knowledge of Chinese fossils came from druggists' collections for it was not until a few years ago that systematic fossil hunting was carried out in China.

In 1926, over twenty years after the first discovery, a Swedish scientist found two more human teeth near Choukoutien. Choukoutien is a little village at the foot of the Western Hills on the border of the Hopei plain. While it is only a few miles by air from Peiping the winding road is about forty miles long. For many years land near the village had been quarried for building materials. In the course of this quarrying old caves were discovered. They had been filled in by soft surface material washed into the fissures which led to them and by the collapse of the cave roofs, so that they had been closed long before the end of prehistoric times. About a million years before they were re-discovered they had opened on the face of the low hills. The teeth were in one of these caves.

In 1929 Dr. Davidson Black found a third tooth while directing excavations at Choukoutien. He was convinced that an entirely new human creature had been discovered and published an account of the new find, naming it the Chinese Man of Peking.

In spite of various stories, paleontologists usually do have something more than one tooth when they announce that they have found a new creature.

Usually they have a few bones less perfect or less important than the tooth. Teeth, however, as we have seen are curiously distinctive. The newly found tooth was compared with those found earlier with all the care given to this kind of work.

No mistake had been made and evidence soon came to light which proved it. At first only skulls were found—a most curious circumstance and one hard to explain—but recently limb-bones have been excavated. These are all fragments, but the fragments are large enough to give some idea of the sizes of the bones and so of the individuals to whom they once belonged. Skulls, teeth, and limb-frag-ments seem to have belonged to forty individuals, old and young, men, women, and children.

The first skull had curiously thick bones so that the brain, when a brain-cast was made, proved smaller than had been expected. More recently found skulls have thinner bones and so the brains are larger. But they are still small and ill-shaped for a human being. For this reason Peking Man must be definitely regarded as one of the most unintelligent members of the early human race. Indeed there is very little choice between him and the Java Ape-man.

He must have looked more human than the Ape-man of Java, however, and this is a good chance to explain how we can speak so definitely about the looks of these long-dead ancestors.

To reconstruct the living face of a fossil skull either the original bones or careful plaster-casts are used. If the bones have been crushed in the process of being fossilized, they must be *most* carefully broken apart and put into their original shape. If that is not possible, new bones must be modeled and put in positions such as they had when their owner was alive. Why the casts must be so carefully made when they are to be hidden will soon be clear.

The amount of flesh over the bones of the face has certain definite proportions in certain places; so cubes, oblongs, or cylinders of cork or some other light, firm material are fastened in those places on the skull. Modeling clay is then put on the skull

55

to the heights indicated by these markers. This makes the correct proportion of flesh, but the expression of the face may be a bit wooden.

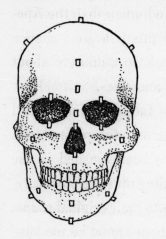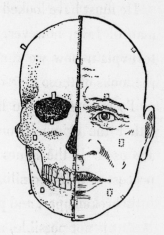

METHOD OF RESTORATION SHOWING FLESH ADDED TO ONE SIDE OF SKULL.

Courtesy of Dr. J. H. McGregor

Usually this work is done by an artist supervised by a scientist to restrain any artistic flights of fancy. Sometimes the scientist is skilled enough to do all the work himself. If not, the artist has his innings for his knowledge is needed to give expression to the face—always providing the proper propor-

56

tions are kept. This is careful labor, consisting sometimes of the position of an eyelid or the twist of the mouth into a smile or a snarl. It is amazing how different the face built on one bony structure is from another built on a different skull.

Hair makes a great change in appearance too. Different wigs tried on different models produce totally unsuspected results. Long, unkempt hair invariably adds a note of wildness to the most civilized head. Add smoothly dressed hair to the most primitive face and, while you might not care to meet him on a dark night, in broad daylight (with appropriate clothes) you would never suspect the distance that separates his life from yours.

Peking Man had made a step toward modern appearance which had nothing to do with his hair—he had much more prominent cheek-bones. Although his brow-ridges were almost as heavy as those of the Java Ape-man and he had an enormously heavy, chinless jaw, those cheek-bones made him look much more human.

57

He was approaching our standards of living in another matter than looks. He used fire. So important is this step that the Greeks, as you know, made it into a fable. To the anthropologist the use of fire requires no fable; it definitely shows a different state of culture—man's entire effort at improving his surroundings that he may live in some better fashion.

That Peking Man used fire there can be no doubt. In the cave where his bones are found there are strata of blackened particles mixed with sand and clay of different colors. Chemistry has proved that the particles are carbon and the colors of sand and clay are due to firing. It seems unlikely that Peking Man had progressed enough to have learned the invaluable knack of *making* fire. His was rather the ability to use what he found—no mean method of improvement. From brands ignited by volcanoes or dropping from forest fires this Man of Peking managed to build a smaller but more permanent blaze in a confined space.

Why Peking Man carried fire into his cave we

may never know. It was not for warmth alone. The climate did not demand a permanent shelter from cold and there is abundant evidence that he did not live in the cave all the time. This is proved by the many other bones of animals which must have used the cave at the same period since their bones are fossilized in the same manner. Some of these bones are those of bears and hyenas. Now there is little chance that such different animals as this advanced primate and those flesh-eaters could have lived in the same cave at the same time—at any rate for long. There must have been various changes of inhabitants. Possibly the fire helped drive away the owners whom the Man of Peking had temporarily dispossessed. We can picture a little group of the tribe sitting uneasily in the flickering light of flames they keep alive. They face a darkness irregularly broken by the gleam of eyes. Constantly one or the other of the tribe changes position as the soft sound of bodies in motion and the padding of feet in the darkness raise the fear that a flanking movement is being attempted by

59

some evicted dweller seeking to regain his stronghold.

Against such attack Peking Man had another resource which proved he had advanced a long way on the road to the present. He had weapons. They were poor weapons but they showed a definite attempt to improve on the weapons bestowed by nature—hands and teeth. These artificial weapons were antlers of deer and roughly chipped flints largely made from chert (a poor grade of waxy, transparent quartz). Rough as these were in manufacture they must have added bite to their maker's blow. They also enabled him to strike from much greater distance for, judging from his brain, Peking Man was right-handed and could throw stones with, probably, considerable accuracy.

The antlers may have been tools as well as weapons. They may have helped to pry the bits of flint from the edge of the larger pieces—"flaking" is the technical term. The many jaws of deer which are found are pretty certain to have been tools and not weapons. They were probably scrapers used

60

in separating flesh from bones. Certain of the flints might have been used in the same way.

Enough game was present to keep many weapons and tools busy: a small deer, a forerunner of our present Axis deer; a musk-ox of a type now extinct; a buffalo likewise vanished from our world. A rhinoceros, only slightly different from his European kin, was among the spoils of chase. There were various small rodents—some rabbits now extinct and a shrew whose descendants still scurry around the home of their ancestors. An elephant is represented among the bones found in the cave and this was the same kind as those which browsed in the forests of Pleistocene India. The animal whose bones are present in the greatest numbers is the deer whose antlers and jaws served as tools. This was not like any of our living deer. It must have looked as if suffering from an attack of mumps for the jaws show a thickening at the curve which must have given their owner the appearance of a swollen face. From this peculiarity this deer has been named the Deer with Thick Bones.

Evidently venison was used for food and Peking Man had acquired a taste for roast marrow. All the bones are split and many of them are charred with fire. But it must not be imagined that this early man had advanced to a stage of cooked food. That is a very advanced stage of culture and Peking Man was far from any state of civilization. Most of his meals were in a natural state and the marrow must have been just a treat roasted at some campfire.

These camp-fires were not always in caves. The climate did not require permanent shelters as some of the cave contents indicate. In it are found the fruits of the hackberry and traces of red-bud wood. Today hackberry grows in moderately arid climates which have streams in the wet seasons. Along those streams a species of elm and poplar have their roots. Not far from the present Choukoutien these same trees have been found; so it seems safe to assume that at the time of the Man of Peking the climate was much as it is now.

Possibly Peking Man followed the courses of

these streams for part of the year, enjoying the shelter of their sparse woods and making small huts along their banks. These huts must have been completely destroyed in a wet season and their owner driven to the caves into which he carried the wood to keep his fires alight as well as to roast the marrow bones.

That Peking Man was a sufficiently good hunter to keep himself supplied with this delicacy seems doubtful. His was not a brain with the skill necessary for real hunting. He could not plan. He must rather have relied upon the attack of a group which co-operated just as a pack of hunting animals acts together in attacking another animal. The effectiveness in group action lay in the fact that Peking Man, himself, was not so very far removed from the prey he was attacking. But besides group attack he must have had another wile. The wounded animal, the weak, the young must have been favorites in his hunting since they would be more surely and more easily overcome.

Apparently it was not animals only which were

attacked. The first bones of Peking Man which were found were skulls and those skulls all bore wounds which had been inflicted when they were not skulls but the heads of living creatures. Moreover, after death those same skulls had been cracked and emptied of their brains. The very few fragments of long-bones show that they, as well as the deer bones, had had their marrow extracted.

So we come to one of the scientific mysteries or what will be a mystery until new facts are discovered. Scientists have divided on the question. As in most mysteries there are two schools of thought each providing a solution. One group says that some creature, more advanced in culture than Peking Man, dismembered the bodies of his victims for cannibalistic purposes. Another group insists that the heads were treated as certain savages today treat the heads they retain—for ceremonial purposes.

To the first group the reply is that there is no evidence that any human creature save Peking Man was present during that time. To the second the answer must be made that savages preserve bones with reverence and no such sign is shown. It seems clear that the contents of the cave were the cast-off spoils of some bloody affray.

The Man of Peking may have been the victim of some of his own kind who belonged to a different group which abhorred the peculiarities of the other group with overwhelming hatred. Possessing temporarily superior peculiarities himself, this unknown hominid left the dismembered remains in the lower cave at Choukoutien and now they give us, hominids of greater superiority, some knowledge of the earliest of our race.

7

BETWEEN MEN

THE next man who seems to be on the line steadily advancing toward the present is found on a different continent. He is a European but no inhabitant of modern Europe. His very existence is a problem and we will understand it better if we make a brief survey of the events which had occurred in Europe before this man's history begins.

The western part of the continent was rather like a huge peninsula attached to eastern Europe which itself almost formed a part of Asia. England was part of this peninsula and through low-lying, partly swampy land covering the present English Channel and the North Sea the slow, sluggish Thames moved to meet a wide, slow-moving Rhine. The Elbe River flowed into the Atlantic.

Europe had not been having so tranquil a time, geologically, as Asia. Just before the Pleistocene began the climate had begun to be strangely cool—strangely, because for hundreds of centuries Europe had been a delightfully warm continent. Now chill struck through the atmosphere. A great natural catastrophe had overtaken the continent—the temperature had dropped. This sounds insignificant but it would take only about ten degrees lower temperature throughout an entire continent to bring perpetual winter over the land. When, after thousands of years of mild climate, the temperature dropped in Pleistocene Europe, glaciers, sheets of living ice thousands of feet thick, gathered in the north and in the Alps and began to move east, west, and south.

Before them traveled wind and rain, and snow and wind accompanied their inexorable advance. Before them and their chilling heralds animals and plants too sought warmer refuges. Since Europe was part of so vast a land-mass both animals and plants could travel far. Only where mountains

67

stretched from east to west shutting off the south, the plants which could not climb their heights died. Besides retreat to Asia retreat to Africa was also possible. Where Gibraltar now stands the two continents met and the sea which is now the Mediterranean was two lakes separated by another bridge of land stretching from the present Italy through Sicily and so to Africa.

The first advance of the ice was not very great but it was an appalling change from a mild climate. Over the African land-bridge wandered millions and millions of animals. Many of the weaker died. Some stayed in Africa and the hardiest, changing sleek hides for rough, woolly covering, moved north again and lingered on the edge of the ice-sheets. For thousands of years there was no seasonal change. Continual winter hung over Europe.

Then the mysterious cause which had lowered the general temperature gradually disappeared. No one yet knows what this cause was. It has been suggested that the elevation of the continents which had been steadily continuing for millions of years

EUROPE AS IT LOOKED HALF A MILLION YEARS AGO. ENGLAND WAS PART OF THE CONTINENT. TWO LARGE LAKES SEPARATED BY A LAND BRIDGE OCCUPIED THE TERRITORY WHERE THE MEDITERRANEAN IS TODAY. NOTE THE LAND BRIDGE CONNECTING AFRICA WITH SPAIN.

might have chilled the world. Another suggestion is that some accumulation of dust or gas in the upper atmosphere had shut off the heating force of the sun's rays. This seems more probable but we are far more certain of the effects than of the real causes.

England did not suffer so heavily from the First Glacial Period—as the first advance of the ice is called—as continental Europe. No ice covered it. Still the temperature became much cooler and its forests changed their trees from palms and warm-weather trees to the mixed forest such as a cool climate has today. When the glaciers retreated and animals and plants began to creep back again, England never regained the semi-tropical trees which had grown there.

It was while the glaciers were making their first advance on Europe that the Ape-man of Java was living in much warmer Asia. Indeed the glaciers in Europe may have helped to make a moister, warmer climate on the neighboring continent. The moisture which wrapped the icy world in snow fell as rain on the southern and eastern lands. So the northern part of Africa was moist and Asia, except in the high mountain region, was a land of comfortable climate. Peking Man lived while the first glaciers were retreating in Europe.

If man had reached Europe before the glaciers we have no fossils to prove it. The anthropoid apes which had lived there a few million years before the Pleistocene began came from a stock differing from man's ancestral line. They were not followed by man-like primates.

There does seem to be other proof, however, that man—possibly such an ancestor as the Java Ape-man—had really reached Europe before the glaciers came. Just possibly he reached there even before the Pleistocene began. The proof of this lies in some extremely crude flint implements which have been found in strata or beds which were there when the glaciers came. We know they were there earlier than the glaciers because the streams of melting glaciers cut through these strata.

As the glaciers melted, quantities of water rushed

toward the sea. The rivers and streams brimmed with foaming, rushing water and literally tore their way seaward. In doing so they cut away the land through which they rushed. These cuts are called terraces for, when they are pointed out by a skilled geologist, they really look like terraces of Nature's making. When the glaciers came again and melted again, another deeper terrace was cut. Indeed with the return and retreat of the third and fourth glaciers the terraces look rather like a series of notches growing smaller near the bottom.

In beds cut through by the first of these terraces extremely crude flint implements have been found. They are so crude that many archaeologists do not believe they are man-made. Other archaeologists whose opinions are equally valuable think that some human hand fashioned them. The second group acknowledges the crudeness and agrees that luck rather than skill shaped the ugly forms. But they believe that human muscles directed the luck.

These flints have been named eoliths (dawn-stones) and they were made by striking the edges of the flint with a stone so that a rough edge was made. Flints which may be eoliths are found near Liége in Belgium and have been found at Cantal in France, but those which have excited the most interest were found at Ipswich, England. An

EOLITHS OF QUARTZ.

archaeologist worked for many years to rouse belief in their human fabrication. Although laughed at in the beginning, his persistence and the number of eoliths from one place at last won him some followers. Today many scientists have slowly come to his opinion. Some human creature—or some almost human creature—seems to have been on the continent of Europe and in England before Peking Man fashioned his crude implements in Asia.

8

THE PILTDOWN MAN OF ENGLAND

EVEN if there is no fossil to prove that any human creatures existed in Europe before the glaciers came, it would not be strange if they had reached there at that time. In a few thousand years some semi-humans must have made the trip from Java, then part of greater Asia, to the northern part of the continent reaching the point where Peking Man was found. From that point to England there was a clear way for any creature capable of walking.

There was ample time too even for so long a march. Between the time of Peking Man in the Pleistocene and that of Piltdown Man, the earliest human ancestor found in England, there are quite a few thousand years. Such a progress would not have been a definite migration. It was a drifting forward by creatures progressing toward manhood as well as toward the west. They must have built half-camps and half-shelters here and there, lived a few weeks or months and moved onward in search of game or adventure. Sometimes, although we have no proof, stray groups remained behind or went off on routes of their own. The movement westward was not realized by the creatures making it any more than they realized the hundreds of years that slipped behind their changing company.

The trail for such a trek would have stretched thousands of miles but it would have been free from barriers. From the Yellow River, already pouring its waters into the Pacific Ocean, the way led to the Caspian Sea. That was much larger than it is now but it was only a small lake in comparison with what it had been. For it had been a vast inland sea. From the Caspian the route lay toward the Black Sea which was also the relic of a larger ocean. Then came the river valleys. Up the valley of the Danube and across to the valley of the Rhine

76

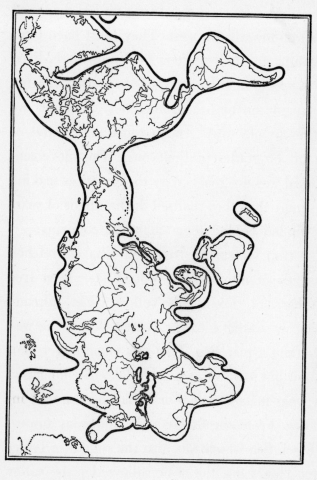

MAP OF THE WORLD HALF A MILLION YEARS AGO. NOTICE THE
LAND BRIDGE CONNECTING ASIA AND NORTH AMERICA.

the way lay clear and the Rhine, flowing through the low-lying land, made a safe route to England. So the unknown ancestors of Europe's first man might have made the journey half a million years ago.

At any rate in 1912 at Piltdown in Sussex, England, a piece of human skull was found. This had been torn out of a gravel bank by men working at road repairs. Some time before a bit of human bone had been found and a sharp lookout had been kept for others. When another piece of bone was found, a still sharper watch was kept by an expert paleontologist and fragments of a skull were discovered. Later, in 1913, part of a lower jaw containing two teeth and a separate canine tooth and bits of nasal bone were recovered from the gravel. When the skull appeared in 1912 there was no doubt that it had belonged to a new and different man from any known and it was named *Eoanthropus dawsoni,* Dawson's Dawn Man, after its discoveror. Like Peking Man, *Eoanthropus* is more often given the name of the place where he was

79

found and is called Piltdown Man.

In 1915, two miles from Piltdown, fragments of a second skull and another lower molar tooth were found. This all sounds very simple and straightforward but the result has been one of the most interesting scientific mysteries which have come to light in the last few years.

The trouble lay with the jaws. Jaws have frequently given trouble and this one certainly did. Some scientists thought it could not have any connection with the skull. But it was found with the skull fragments. It is fossilized in the same way and so must have lain as long in the same earth. But it is heavy, chinless, and quite ape-like. The teeth in it are primitive and show an ape-like pattern.

But the skull surely belonged to a man! It is almost like a skull of the present day—such a one as should never have had that jaw attached to it. True, the bones were thick so that the brain was smaller than might have been expected from the outside of the skull. For that and for other very technical reasons it has been suggested that the

Piltdown skull might be that of a woman but this opinion has never really been accepted.

Some scientists still feel that jaw and skull belong to different creatures. Their contentions go so far as to claim that the bones are left from a struggle between the owner of the skull and a much less developed creature, possessor of jaw and teeth. Against this theory is the discovery made later at some distance from the first find. Granted that the first bones are the remains of a battle royal, there could hardly have been two such battles within a few miles of each other each of which left nearly the same records behind. That is not credible.

Another trouble has been in determining the age of the gravels in which the bones were found. There was a feeling that they might belong to a later time. They were undoubtedly laid down by streams during a warm period but perhaps not during the first retreat of the ice.

Peking Man's discovery makes it much more likely that a similar creature could have been in

England at about the same time, as we have already said.

Piltdown Man is just such a human as *might* have developed in the thousands of years it would have taken a group of semi-humans to make that long march from Asia to Europe. Because we are sure of Peking Man, the Dawn Man of England becomes a much more acceptable member of society than when he was first greeted. Since Peking Man has a definitely known place, England's Piltdown Man has a logical place as his relative living on another continent. He not only existed—as his bones proved—but he is now granted scientific reasons for such an existence.

While the controversy was raging, however, several efforts were made to restore the fragments into a complete skull and to clothe that skull with the appearance of life. Then the controversy over jaw and skull reached its height. The skull was much broken. If the jaw were used, the skull must be adapted to muscles necessary for its operation. This of course involved the arrangement of the frag-

PILTDOWN MAN.

Courtesy of Dr. J. H. McGregor

ments in a very different position from that needed
if no heavy muscles were to be attached. All in all
the controversy used up reams of paper and many
pounds of modeling clay. No one is absolutely posi-
tive even now but at least a working truce, in which
the arrival of Peking Man played a part, has been
reached.

This gives us a human with a nearly vertical
forehead, no heavy ridges over the eyes such as
Peking Man had, a rather heavy jaw which seems
to protrude somewhat owing to the setting of the
teeth. We can be sure from the thrust of jaw and
heaviness of bone that the neck was short and thick,
because heavy muscles would have been needed to
hold the skull at the angle it must have had in relation to the vertebrae. Given a few realities anatomists can do a good deal. They do not attempt to
give us a picture of Piltdown Man in full length,
however, although it is safe to assume that a body
built to uphold such a head would be short and
stocky. That is mere guess, of course, but there is
little guess as to what went on in Piltdown Man's

brain. The cast of that proved larger than a woman's of some primitive race such as the native Australian but smaller than the brain of a living European woman and much smaller than most masculine brains. This last is one of the reasons for thinking the skull may have been that of a woman. This cast also shows the brain specialist that Piltdown Man had very little power of putting cause and effect together.

Such acts as flint-chipping could be performed roughly but Piltdown Man could not remember any tricks learned in the process. To profit by experience was beyond him. Each thing was new save in the way things seemed familiar. One camp site might seem more comfortable or even better than another but there would be no real remembrance of any time when it had been visited before.

Since Piltdown Man lived in a time when the climate was mild, there was little need of shelter. And, since we cannot think of one lone denizen of a great continent, we must think of scattered groups of man-like creatures living over the entire land mass of Eurasia (Europe and Asia combined). They probably chose camp sites at the foot of cliffs near rivers where water was easily gotten and where the flints they worked were most easily reached. Probably some of the camps were on the slopes of hills near springs and not too far from some flint outcrop. Camp-fires, replenished by clearing the brush from the camp, must have sent smoke up into the clear skies of many miles of land.

Hunting was carried on near these camps, for bones have been found. Considering Piltdown Man's probable mental limitations, much of it must have been done with traps. These would have snared the unwary animal—often the young preceding the mother toward some drinking spot. Since Piltdown Man killed creatures far too big to have yielded to such mass attacks as a group of his kind could have made, it is fairly certain that the very big game must have been captured by pitfalls of some kind.

There was certainly enough game to give a great variety of sport. There was one of the largest ele-

phants which ever lived—the Southern Mammoth. There were two different rhinoceroses living then and Piltdown Man must have heard them snorting as they waded in the slow streams which meandered over the country now covered by the North Sea and the English Channel. A huge beaver made its home in these same streams and the quiet evenings must have carried the sounds of its activities.

Of course there was a hyena among the beasts. Apparently a scavenger was always part of the animal population in Pleistocene Europe. There were big cats, not so large as the saber-toothed cats, for whom the hyena must have been a follower. Hyenas, cats, and Piltdown Man must all have preyed upon the different kinds of wild cattle which watered in the streams and fed on the abundant grass.

Piltdown Man must have set traps and fashioned flints by day. At night, listening to the scamper of driven deer and the pad of stalking feet, he hugged his fire and hoped that this fear dispeller would last until the dawn. So, living the life of primitive hunter and flint worker, we can think of Piltdown Man as the denizen of a distant world—the earliest of Europeans but only one member of what must have been a far-flung population. Of this we have proof on two continents.

9

PRE-CHELLEAN
AND CHELLEAN INTERLUDE

THIS proof of man's existence in the warm world between glaciers lies in the presence of his flints and not his fossils. "By their works ye shall know them" was written in a very different connection but the words are true of these vanished men.

Flints were known long before they were recognized as objects manufactured by man. Before Caesar invaded England a Roman poet said that man used stone implements before he had metal tools and weapons. Sixteen hundred years later an Englishman spoke of flints as "weapons used by Britons before the art of making arms of brass and iron was known." Later still a Dane who had devoted his life to studying early man suggested that there had actually been a Stone Age—a time when man *manufactured* weapons and tools of stone.

From that time more and more attention was paid to flints. Before many fossils of men had been found and long before there was enough material known to give an idea of their physical development, archaeologists had a definite idea of the order in which different kinds of flints had been made and of their places in geologic time. A group of flints made during one period and differing from any group made during another period is called a "culture" or industry. The name of each culture is usually taken from the place where it was first found or where it is found at its best.

As a whole these different cultures are grouped into two great periods: the Old Stone Age, the period of unpolished flints; and the New Stone Age when implements were carefully finished and polished. Within these two main divisions are a number of cultures arranged chronologically, each culture showing change in the types of implements or methods of manufacture. Often archaeologists speak as if flints were things quite apart from the men who made them. This is absurd, of course, for it is obviously a case of no men no manufactures. It has come about because sometimes worked flints are the only proof of men's existence and because the opportunities for their study have been much greater than the opportunities for studying fossil man himself.

Before we go much further it is best to stop a minute to be sure we understand how flints (the implements) were made from flint (the mineral). We will also become acquainted with the special meaning of the words used in describing their manufacture. The rough lump of brownish-gray stone from which the tool takes its name is a "nodule." It varies in size from a piece two or three inches long to one almost the length of your forearm. A prehistoric tool-maker "worked" this nodule by striking it along the lines where it broke most successfully. This was a matter of skill and experience and some of the long-forgotten workshop sites are piled with discards spoiled in the making. A ham-

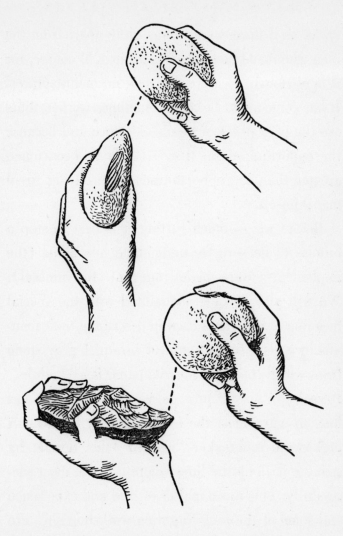

USE OF THE HAMMER-STONE IN MAKING FLINTS.

mer-stone, originally a natural stone of size suitable for grasping, was used for this purpose. The
piece struck off was a "flake" and the remainder
of the nodule became a "core." A weapon made
from a single lump of flint is called a core-weapon
or core-form. The flakes varied in size with the core
from which they were struck and with the manner
used in making them. Some flakes were the size of
a thumb nail; some were several inches long. But
whatever the size may be, flake can be told from
core because the flake has a swelling and the core
a cavity. These occur just below the point where the
final blow causing separation was delivered.

As time progressed, many flakes were struck
from a single core. When the flint-worker became
skillful enough to plan real edges for his weapons,
he used another smaller bit of flint or a piece of
bone and chipped or forced smaller flakes or chips
from the edges by pressure. This is called "pressure
flaking" or "pressure chipping."

The earliest flints found at Ipswich belong some
thousands of years earlier than any known human

fossils in Europe. That is why the dissenting group of scientists refused to consider them as anything except flints shaped by the chances of nature. The flaked flints found with Peking Man and Piltdown Man are crude in the extreme but they are undeniably altered from their original state not by chance but by purpose. They are hand-made. At Choukoutien there is also a charred deer's antler which it is thought *might* have been used to pry flakes from nodules. Such a tool is a very important innovation. To realize that it was possible to improve nature's weapons, whether claws or stones, was a long step forward. To think of implements to aid in making these improvements was an amazing advance in the history of our forebears. We pride ourselves on our modern labor-saving devices and gadgets. There were human creatures, even before the dawn of history, who had the same ideas and the ability to give those ideas concrete forms.

The next group of flints in the line of progress was given the technical name of Pre-Chellean or Early Chellean. (Chellean flints belong to a later

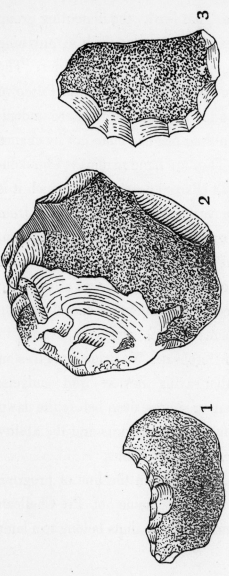

EOLITHS FOUND IN ENGLAND.

1. SIDESCRAPER TYPE—CONCAVE EDGE

2. HAMMER-STONE TYPE

3. SIDESCRAPER TYPE—CONVEX EDGE

Courtesy of Dr. Nelson and the American Museum of Natural History

time although they were found first. They were named for the town of Chelles in France where they were first found.) These Early Chellean flints are scattered over France, found in Spain, discovered in Belgium, and dug up in England. They are also found in Africa. But of their makers no single bone has ever been discovered.

The workmanship of these implements is a little less crude than that shown by the implements found with Peking Man. Among the pieces is a weapon which was to last, although in improved form, for thousands of years. This was made from a single piece of flint and so is a core-form or core-weapon. From one "face" (side) of this core the unknown makers struck off a few rough, badly-planned flakes. Although no hammer-stones have been found—that is, none of manufactured shape—a hammer-stone must have been used. The result was a rough, oval weapon about half the size of a man's hand. One end had a badly made point; the opposite end was not touched and so made a good hand hold. For this reason the French who first named it called the weapon a "coup-de-poing" which we translate as hand ax or cleaver. Besides the cleaver the Early Chelleans made a few crude tools from flakes. These flakes were struck from cores slightly larger than those used for the cleavers, so that the finished implements—if such crude things can be called finished—were nearly the same size. Like the cleaver, the flake tools were edged from one side only and most clumsily at that. They were probably intended as knives and scrapers for lighter work than the cleavers, and were not intended as weapons.

Flint workers began their trade earlier in Africa than in Europe because, since Africa had no glaciers except in the high mountains, the climate was comfortable. Even there the men who made the flints left no fossils to prove their existence. But just because there are none we get some idea of how those men must have lived although we can get no idea of how they may have looked. If the glaciers wiped out all traces of their bodily existence in Europe and a warm but moist climate did

100

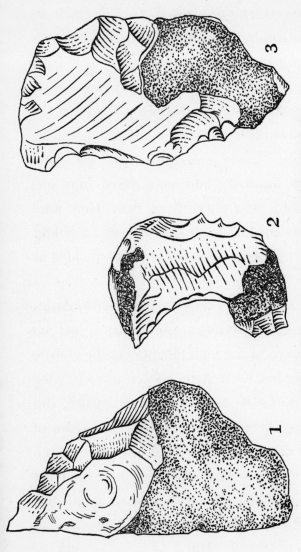

PRE-CHELLEAN CORE AND FLAKE IMPLEMENTS.

1. POINTED CORE IMPLEMENT WITH HAND HOLD
2. SIDESCRAPER WITH CHIPPED EDGE
3. CLEAVER WITH HAND HOLD

Courtesy of Dr. Nelson and the American Museum of Natural History

the same thing in Africa, it would be pretty safe to say that the bones which never became fossils must have lain on open ground when their owners died; so they had no chance to become fossilized. At any rate none have yet been found—no unknown maker of Pre-Chellean flints seems to have fallen into a water hole or crawled away to die in a hole where the wind would have covered him with earth and the rain would have turned earth and bones, constantly covered by more and more earth, into fossils. Now people dying in the open probably lived in the open too. So we can imagine these unknown flint workers as a people of hunting habits—why else make cleavers?—living in open air camps, moving from place to place as camp sites became too soiled, game moved on, or flints were less easy to find. Perhaps when the weather was particularly warm and when they were shifting camps, they lived without shelters. They may even have followed the habits of their not so distant ancestors and made tree-nests or platforms. When the weather was less comfortable or a fairly permanent camp was made, they may have constructed rude huts of boughs and leaves.

During these long centuries both Europe and northern Africa were pleasant places in which to live. In Europe the glaciers had retreated to mountain tops and to the far north. In Africa, where the moisture which fell as snow in Europe had fallen as rain, the plains were grassy and there were little chuckling streams. Game abounded and none of the arid conditions of today were known.

In Europe the streams, fed from the melted snows, ran foaming and roaring, cutting out terraces on their banks as they wore their beds to different levels. The hardier animals had moved northward with the retreating snows, for warm winds brought no comfort to their thick coats. As the browsing improved, the less hardy re-crossed the land-bridges from their southern retreats and again filled the continent they had forgotten.

This period of re-established warmth may have lasted for more than a hundred thousand years. Certainly the animals found at its close differ from those living when it began and it takes a very long time indeed for an animal to alter his teeth and bony structure. But this time of warmth and plentiful hunting was an interlude, not an established condition. Again chilling winds warned and the animals followed their favorite food as the plants retreated southward pushed by cold winds blowing from the north. Once more land-bridges were crowded with the seekers of warmth, while the hardy creatures who had followed the retreating ice moved into the feeding grounds their less hardy companions deserted. Again walls of ice moved southward and this time they were heralded by even colder winds; they moved farther south and they stayed there a much longer time. The Second Glacial Period, or the second advance of the glaciers, once more filled Europe with perpetual winter.

Yet these glaciers were not to remain there. The atmosphere changed again, and more slowly than the first time sun, warmth, animals, and hunters returned to Europe as the glaciers again withdrew

105

to the north and to the mountain tops. Streams filled with icy water once more tore through the land, cutting a second series of terraces, and when after several hundred centuries the stream banks were again livable a new set of flint workers pitched their camps there.

The first discovery of a camp used by these new flint workers was made by a French archaeologist in the middle of the last century. Officially the archaeologist was a customs inspector, and he noticed that the men working the gravel pits of his district turned up flints not of nature's making. In this way the site of the old open air camp at Chelles in France was discovered.

The Chellean flint workers had not developed much greater deftness in their craft than their unknown predecessors; but they had progressed a little and they chose their material with more care. They used their hammer-stones to strike flakes from *both* sides of more carefully selected flint nodules and so made cleavers with edges which, though still poor, were sharper. A few smaller flakes

106

were struck from the edges themselves which was a further improvement. While the base was always left unchipped to make a good hand hold, the form of the sharpened end varied. Some had a sharpened *edge* opposite the unflaked butt. These may have been used as choppers to cut roots or branches. The more usual form was a pointed oval. Some of these have a rather acute point; some taper gradually. Some of the almond-shaped pieces were longer than wide and thinner than the usual cleavers. These were probably general utility pieces— knives, daggers, borers, and scrapers all in one. It is just possible that some of the cleavers were fitted into wooden handles but, if so, not a trace of wood has survived.

Besides these core implements the Chelleans began to use the flakes for tools and weapons. Their cleavers were larger than those the Pre-Chelleans had made, and the flakes were some two inches long. These flakes were chipped along one or more edges on both faces just as the cores had been flaked from each face. In all the tools you can see

107

the "basic patent" of the cleaver but they were made with more thought for their use. One was blunted and flattened except for the very tip which had an edge. This may have been a scraper for skins although we have no proof that it was used in dressing hides. All the implements show increased ingenuity on the part of their makers— an effort to adapt the same material to different needs.

It is not surprising that more is not known of the men who shaped these flints. If, as climate and absence of fossils suggest, they lived in open camps probably shifting from place to place as game moved and flints were less easily found, there was little chance for their bones to be preserved. Prowling hyenas and the destruction of weather would soon leave no trace. What we know of the climate is learned from the bits of fossil twigs and leaves found in the strata which held the flints. These show that ash, oak, birch, linden, and hazel trees were growing when the Chelleans were living. Such trees are trees of temperate climates and would not

108

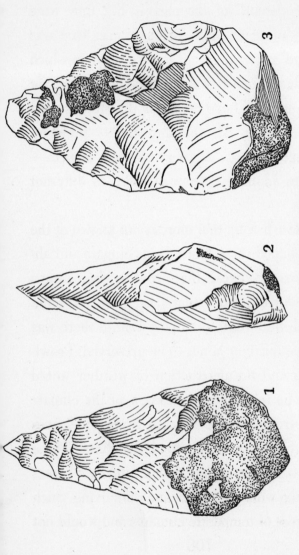

CHELLEAN CORE IMPLEMENTS.

1. POINTED CLEAVER
2. CHOPPER-LIKE CLEAVER
3. OVAL CLEAVER WITH HAND HOLD

Courtesy of Dr. Nelson and the American Museum of Natural History

have grown in the full warmth of an interglacial period.

The animals whose bones lie in the same strata also show that change was on its way. The elephant is not the same as that found in Pre-Chellean beds. A very large deer, some smaller kin, a wild bison, the ever-present hyena, have left their bones with Chellean flints. A lion, related to those living today, and a cave bear, also an ancestor of some European bears, were alive. A small horse browsed on the plains. The bones of these creatures were preserved in mud when the glaciers returned and wiped out all traces of the open camps in which the Chelleans had lived. Only their tools, hard stones, survived the geologic hardships of Europe and the dryness of the African desert which followed the mild, interglacial period. In Europe dryness did not follow the retreat of the ice. Conditions were better for the preservation of fossils. And by very good fortune we have a fossil record of what we believe is one Chellean hunter.

111

10

HEIDELBERG MAN — CHELLEAN?

SCIENTISTS refuse to say that the human fossil found in beds of the same age as those in which Chellean flints are found *is* actually that of a Chellean flint worker because no Chellean flints were found with it. If you want to be very scientific, you can say no Chellean flints were "associated with it." Moreover, no scientist worth his salt ever said one fossil represented a group of people, and unfortunately from the day it was found to the present no other fossil of that period has been discovered. Yet, since it is unquestionably of the same age as the Chellean flints, it is not really unsafe to believe that the single jawbone found is that of a Chellean hunter.

In 1907 this jawbone was found by laborers

working in a sand quarry at Mauer near Heidelberg in Germany. It was found seventy-nine feet below the present surface of the ground in what must have been the bank of an ancient river. The sands and gravels of the Pleistocene age which fill these quarries concealed the bones of many animals in their depths and these were such animals as lived in a comparatively mild climate. Wolf, wildcat, lion, and bear left their bones in the Mauer sands. The hyena is there also. Beaver had lived in the pools of the streams. A deer with wide-spreading antlers was plentiful. Two forms of wild oxen wallowed in the mud of the river banks. One was the European bison or wisent, a few of which are still living on private game preserves; the other, the aurochs, was known to Julius Caesar as the urus but is now extinct. The so-called Etruscan rhinoceros, first found in Etruria, fed on the grassy edges and open plains. A fleet herd of little horses, called the Mosbach Horse from the place where their bones were first discovered, had kicked up their heels near the rhinoceros. A wild boar rooted under the trees, and

113

moose and elephant nibbled at their branches. The fossilized bones of all these have been found. Only man, dweller of the open, found no damp resting place to preserve his bones.

For twenty years the quarries in and near Mauer had been watched. Since Chellean flints had been known for a long time, paleontologists were on the look-out for their makers. If the single jaw which rewarded the long wait seems very poor compensation, its discoverer is still the only man who found the only bone which is likely to have been the fossil of a Chellean flint worker.

That this lower jaw was a fragment of a new type of man Dr. Schoetensack, its discoverer, was quick to realize. He gave it the name of Heidelberg Man from the famous town near which it was found, but the specimen is also often referred to as the Mauer Jaw.

The jaw is enormously heavy and very large. There is no chin prominence and this suggests ape-like relationships. But the teeth are definitely human, with no high canine teeth, and the dental

114

arch, the shape formed by the curve of the teeth as set in the jaw, is also human. Neither arch nor teeth are very different from those of certain primitive men now living. Only the jaw itself is immensely heavier than any known.

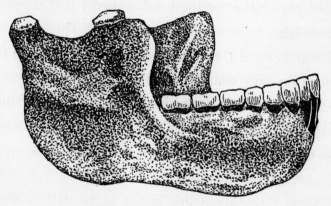

THE HEIDELBERG JAW.

It is the dental arch which gives us knowledge about other parts of the face of Heidelberg Man. Lower teeth must have had upper teeth closing on them. These upper teeth must have been arranged in an upper jaw. The lower jaw must have fitted into bones made for this purpose. One of the great peculiarities of the Mauer Jaw is its massive upright

115

part which anatomists call the ramus. It is unlike any other jaw and demands something special in the way of an arch to accommodate it. In planning such an arch anatomists are led into making provision for the muscles which must have fitted on it and also higher on the head, in order that Heidelberg Man might chew his coarse food. This leads to the next step: the discovery that such muscles and such an arch could not have been possible if the cheek-bones had sloped inward as did those of the Ape-man of Java. Heidelberg Man had much more prominent cheek-bones and consequently a very much broader face.

One thing about this jaw is particularly pleasing to scientists. There would seem to be *no* doubt, even to the most skeptical, that it is definitely related to the jaw of the next human being whose bones are found throughout Europe and in Africa. Scientists love ordered succession. Their creed is that result must have a cause. Piltdown Man was a completely unrelated creature. He seemed to have neither ancestor nor descendant. Heidelberg Man is in better case. One specimen is very little to reason from, but it does seem plain that the Mauer Jaw is such a jaw as the ancestor of the next human, Neandertal Man, should have had.

It is the fact that one specimen is not sufficient basis for general conclusions that makes Heidelberg Man a doubtful member of the Chelleans. No flints were found with the jaw. Even if they had been, the same doubt as to the conclusions to be drawn from a single find would have held good. One discovery is not proof. But certainly all other things—geologic age, probable relationship, indications of ancestry—point in one direction.

The strata in which the jaw was found belonged to a warm climate; Chellean man made his flints in such a period. The age of the gravels is right for Chellean age even though no flints were found. The animal fossils are of types which must have lived during those times. Perhaps it cannot be proved as scientists know proof, but it seems quite safe to think of Heidelberg Man as the sole representative of the Chellean workers of flints.

117

11

NEANDERTAL MAN—DENIZEN OF THE WORLD

ANOTHER advance of ice wiped out all other evidences of the Chellean hunters. Coolness had indeed been stealing over much of their world for fifteen or twenty thousand years before the ice again actually invaded northern Europe. Toward the end of these thousands of years it must have been too cold for any unfurred creature to exist, and a few thousands of years after that walls of ice were once again covering great sections of the continent.

This time the ice did not come so far south as it had in the interval between Piltdown Man's age and the world of Heidelberg Man; nor did it linger so long. It came far enough and lasted long enough, however, to make many changes in Europe's plants

118

and animals. Those which survived had had time enough to change many of their characters—to become different species. Many, retreating to warmer places, never reappeared in the western world. One snail whose fossil shells are found in Chellean heaps moved to another hemisphere and lived on there into our own day.

It was a world at once very old and almost new into which a new human being, Neandertal Man, made his entrance. It had been wiped clean of its past so far as human existence was concerned. Man, if he retreated to Africa and Asia, left no records of bone to tell the tale. But once again we must remember that the moisture which fell as snow in Europe was rain on much of the other continents. Bone, exposed to moisture in uncovered places, rots as the years pass. Since the evidence of durable flints remains, we know that man must have been in Africa and in Asia and from one of these sources must have returned to Europe when the weather permitted human beings to live there.

The first proof of a new race was actually found

at Gibraltar in 1848 but for sixty years no one recognized that the skull found there was anything except the skull of a man.

The first recognized evidence of another race of mankind was found in 1856 by some workmen digging in the ravine of Neandertal near Düsseldorf. They unearthed several arm and leg bones, the top of a skull, parts of the shoulder bones and pelvis. Still they aroused little interest and only part of them were saved. These were placed in the museum at Bonn. Later a skilled anatomist examined them. He recognized that they were bones of a new race of mankind and gave them the name of the Man of Neandertal.

The bones were unquestionably human. But they were so unlike the bones of living men that some scientists felt they had belonged to an abnormal type of man. In 1858 an exhaustive study of the problem was published, so full of careful detail that few people remained unconvinced that a new, strange, but normal human being had been discovered.

About the time that Darwin's "Origin of Species" was published, a group of famous English scientists examined the bones at Bonn and declared their belief that Neandertal Man was a true human who had lived in an interglacial period. Any questions which had remained unanswered were replied to when in 1913 a new monograph appeared. This was so complete a study that it is not likely anything of importance remains unsaid.

This famous paper was not based on the original material but on a much later discovery made in France. Indeed during the years between 1848 and 1913 enough skeletons were discovered to prove that the Man of Neandertal—or rather his contemporaneous kin—had lived on the larger part of the western hemisphere and some of the eastern. In Europe discoveries have been made in Germany, Belgium, Spain, the Channel Islands, Italy, Jugoslavia, and the Crimea, as well as in France where a famous skeleton was found at La Chapelle-aux-Saints in Corrèze.

Skeletons, or portions of them, have been found

121

in Palestine. In 1938 a skull was found in Asia. Flints such as those found with some of the bones had been known for some time. Probably the discovery of even more skeletons over a wider range of territory is only a matter of time.

These skeletons all belonged to a race which spread over three continents during many centuries. They are found with the bones of animals which lived thousands of years apart. We reckon that seventy thousand years must have passed while the Neandertals dominated the world. Not only the animals changed; man himself changed. All the skeletons grouped as Neandertal people resemble each other more than they resemble the skeletons of any other known race of man, but those found at the end of this long period are not exactly the same as those found at its beginning. Many show such change that, half a century ago, scientists would not have hesitated to declare them representatives of new types of man. Now, however, so much has been learned about the variations within one race—the changes possible to a great group of people—and so much has been found out about the Neandertals themselves that all these varying skeletons are identified as members of one race. We can think of Neandertal Man as living in small groups, each with its particular territory, which all formed a related population scattered over the world just as modern man is now distributed.

Neandertal Man is a comfort to the scientists. He is just such a man as the successor to Heidelberg Man should be, particularly if, as we believe, he is one of Heidelberg's descendants. He is short, being little over five feet, and the women and children are particularly small. One fifteen-year-old boy whose skeleton was found at Le Moustier, France, was less than five feet tall. Such measurements are based upon estimates made from the length of the long-bones (thighs to us). Much work on living men has proved that the total height bears a definite relation to the length of the limb-bones and in this manner the height of the Neandertals has been estimated.

The shape of the Neandertal skull is oval and

the brain size varies considerably. The head is curiously low too from the ear-opening to the top of the skull. The forehead retreats and the Neandertals still had brow-ridges over their eyes. Unlike the Ape-man of Java and Peking Man the ridges of the Neandertals did not extend across the forehead. The eyes were far apart and deeply set. The nose was outstanding and, while not negroid in shape, spread widely at the base. The cheeks sloped inward and the arch which held the lower jaw was heavy. That jaw was as chinless as that of Heidelberg Man, while the molar teeth are more nearly even in size than is usual in modern man. They also have a curious construction. The pulp extends much farther toward the roots than is known in other men.

While the neck is heavier than that of modern people, it is not much heavier than that of any primitive man who has spent his life in a forest peering through trees. This invariably adjusts the head to a slightly different angle. The face of Neandertal Man projects forward, the huge palate

124

NEANDERTAL MAN.

Courtesy of Dr. J. H. McGregor

and heavy jaw doing much to add to the impression.

The limbs are heavy. The forearm is short in comparison with the full length of the arm, and the shin is short when measured against the whole length of the leg. Thumb and great toe are interesting. The thumb is as well developed as it is today. The big toe is very much what ours is when, as children, we have enjoyed a long summer without shoes. It could be used much more easily than a grown-up's toe could now, but it could never be compared with a great ape's for dexterity.

The foot, in points only noticeable to a specialist, had not quite reached the stage of development which ours has. This is a matter of the exact proportions of some of the smaller bones and is too technical for us. It has been commonly believed that Neandertal Man could not—or did not—walk erect; that his knees were slightly bent. In view of all the recent researches we must change our minds, for this has certainly not been proved. It is possible that he had as upright a carriage as we have ourselves.

All in all Neandertal Man differs from modern man rather in matters seen by a specialist than in appearances a layman notes. To us he was just a short, heavy-bodied, short-necked, awkward man, probably a little hairier than modern man but not nearly so hairy as a "freak." To the anatomist he appears a very different person.

There is one interesting fact revealed by the brain and the skeleton. The brain, while much inferior to living man, shows that Neandertal Man was capable of speech. The bones of the mouth indicate that the attachment of the tongue and throat muscles was extremely weak. This may have meant that he did not use much more in the line of vocal expression than Peking Man. Speech, experts tell us, is made of two efforts—natural expression and attempts to mark shades of meaning. The first is purely physical and consists of little more than the sounds made in emotions such as fear, anger, surprise, excitement, curiosity, and others. These sounds are produced largely in the throat. A child, unable to talk, has such means of expressing its

128

opinions. Often the body uses a sort of pantomime in an unconscious effort to make the meaning clear.

The next step is probably the unconscious twisting of the tongue in sympathy with the twisting body. Gradually this becomes a definite effort to modify the sounds produced in the throat. In such a way articulate speech, the invention of the brain, is born. Neandertal Man *may* have reached that stage but it seems unlikely. He probably made more sounds than Peking Man and sounds which expressed his meaning more clearly, but speech as we mean the word was still to come.

Neandertal Man probably had more opportunities to exercise speech than did Peking Man. The latter, if it is safe to judge from the still scanty remains, had not progressed socially beyond the family state. Of course this does not mean just mother, father, and children. Like Sir Joseph Porter there were the sisters and the cousins—if not the aunts—but they most certainly were not "reckoned up by dozens." Peking Man lived in a rather large group. The remains of Neandertal Man convince us that he had gone beyond this. His group was a larger one as his camps and caves show us. He probably had the beginning of social organization, which only means that two leaders in a group spell trouble and therefore actual leadership of some sort is trusted to one man.

As to his implements, they were so much of an improvement over those of Heidelberg Man and there were so many new weapons and ways of manufacture that it is easier to give them a chapter almost all to themselves.

12

NEANDERTAL MAN—ACHEULIAN AND MOUSTERIAN CULTURES

THE Neandertal race lived for a very long time, far longer than modern man has been on the earth. Seventy-five thousand years—or about that number—are thought to have elapsed while they dominated the world. Those were years of changing conditions which gave them great opportunities to develop different styles of implements and methods of manufacture. Consequently they made changes and improvements. Some of the specially styled weapons were made in certain sections of various continents but two large groups of implements, called Acheulian and Mousterian, are found on three continents in strata belonging to periods separated by a long interval.

Of these, the Acheulian are the earlier and the name comes from St. Acheul in France where this particular type of implements was discovered. At this place there had been an open air camp on the river bank. When this was carefully excavated it showed that this same site had been used as a camp by different people twice before. This is proved by the fact that as the excavations went downward they uncovered first Chellean and then Pre-Chellean flints, in just that order, in strata under the Acheulian-filled layer.

The Pre-Chellean flints were in strata covered by Chellean-filled gravels and those in turn were covered by the still later Acheulian beds. All three were the kind of formations which geologists tell us must have been left by waters calming down after they had been on a rampage. Three times this had happened, and other evidence places Acheulian flints in the Third Interglacial Period. So we can reason that three different human races had come to this camp site as to a new, glacier-cleaned spot, attracted by its closeness to a stream where game

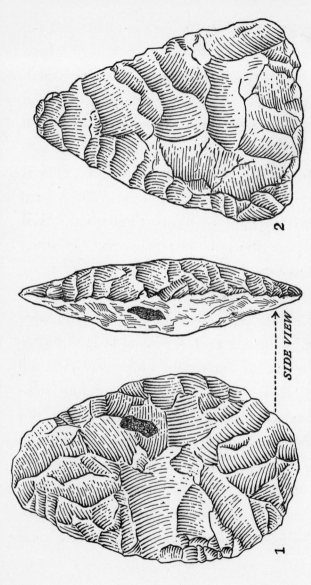

TYPICAL ACHEULIAN CORE IMPLEMENTS.

1. CLEAVER WITH SIDE VIEW
2. CLEAVER POSSIBLY USED AS WEAPON

Courtesy of Dr. Nelson and the American Museum of Natural History

SIDE VIEW

came to drink and to the flint outcrop which even three glaciers could not wear away.

Since there were no human fossils at St. Acheul we have no proof that any of these three groups, each over a hundred and fifty thousand years apart, had overlapped one into another as might happen in an Indian camp where great-great-great-grand-children have lived on the same spot as their ancestors. The only reason we have for supposing this *might* have happened is the flints made here and particularly the flints made by the Chelleans and the later Acheulians. The Acheulian flints are made in such a way that it seems as if their makers *must* have learned the technique of the Chelleans because their own tricks of the trade are certainly improvements upon that earlier work.

The famous cleaver is one of the most common implements of the Acheulian period but it is a much improved cleaver. The edges are chipped on *both* faces and are much straighter and sharper. Flake scrapers and knives of patterns already familiar to us from the Chellean period were used

MAN'S FIRST MILLION YEARS

PLEISTOCENE PERIOD		OLD STONE AGE (Paleolithic)	
Glacial advance (1)	1,000,000 B.C.		Java Ape-man
Glacial retreat	600,000 B.C.		Peking Man / Piltdown Man / Pre-Chellean
Glacial advance (2)	450,000 B.C.	OLD STONE AGE	Heidelberg Man / Chellean
Glacial retreat		(Paleolithic)	
Glacial advance (3)	125,000 B.C.		Neandertal Man / Acheulian / Mousterian
Glacial retreat			
Glacial advance (4)	75,000 B.C.		
Glacial retreat	50,000 B.C.		Grimaldi Race

Cro-Magnons	13,500 B.C.	(slow and uneven in different parts of Europe)
Aurignacian	10,000 B.C. *mesolithic*	
Solutrean	8,500 B.C.	
Magdalenian		
Azilian	7,500 B.C.	
Tardenoisian		
Modern Man	6,500 B.C.	
Maglemose	6,000 B.C.	
New Stone Age (Neolithic)	5,500 B.C.	**RECENT TIME**
Copper Age	2,500 B.C.	
Bronze Age	1,500 B.C.	
Iron Age begun	500 B.C.	**HISTORIC TIME**

but, like the cleavers, they were improved in manufacture. In an abandoned camp—evidently a workshop—at Caddington in Bedfordshire, England, some of the flints had been left in such a fashion that it was possible to fit some of the flakes back into the edges from which they had been struck. This made it possible to study the methods used and the tools by which the double edges had been produced.

This and other like discoveries have shown that the work was carried on in open air camps scattered along streams or near flint outcrops. As the fossil plants and animals show, cold airs were becoming sharp and strong. Some parts of Europe were not only cold but dry, and glaciers began to gather again in the north. Man was driven to temporary shelters under overhanging rocks which retained the heat of the sun and reflected the heat of the camp-fires. The fact that so many sites of camp-fires are found indicates that at last fire could be made when man willed. The legend which the Greeks invented so many, many thousands of years later had become reality. Undoubtedly Neandertal Man made his fires with much labor and difficulty but he made them. Probably, since he was a flint worker, he had seen the spark flicker on the struck flint and had at last learned to put it to use.

As centuries passed and the cold became more bitter the shelter of grottoes was sought. The last advance of the ice sheets was beginning and the Neandertals, perhaps sturdier than the Heidelberg race, and certainly better equipped with fire, prepared to withstand the increasing cold whose cause they were completely unable to understand. Permanent shelters were sought and there, with hunting forays and trips to secure flint, they developed the new and better made group of flints called Mousterian.

That name comes from the tiny cave of Le Moustier on the Vézère River in Dordogne, France. This natural shelter is in a cliff back of the present village. It had been known for a long time but its name became especially famous in 1862. It was then that a French archaeologist, de Mortillet, determined to do for flints what Linnaeus had done for animals—arrange them in groups. So he wrote his famous "Essay on the Classification of Caves and Rock-shelters Based on the Results Produced by Man." He gave the flints found at Le Moustier the name Mousterian. This actual shelter had been used before the Mousterian Age and was used continually during that period. As late as 1908 it yielded another bit of information as we shall find out.

The Mousterian tools and weapons differ very much from those of the Chellean and Acheulian periods. Previous methods of striking off flakes had been a little hit-and-miss. The Neandertals of the Mousterian Age developed more precision. Flint nodules—rough, natural lumps of flint—were chosen carefully, flakes were struck from both sides more carefully, and the edges were made still better by final chipping along the margins. The edges were the best yet produced and although the finished products were smaller than earlier implements they were better fitted for special uses.

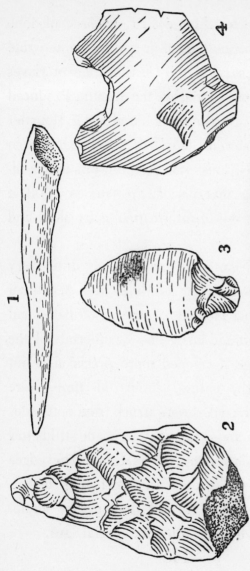

TYPICAL MOUSTERIAN IMPLEMENTS.

1. BONE IMPLEMENT
2. CLEAVER
3. POINTED FLAKE WITH CHIPPED STEM
4. NOTCHED SIDESCRAPER

Courtesy of Dr. Nelson and the American Museum of Natural History

A great change took place in the form of the weapons. The cleaver became smaller and smaller. At last it disappeared. After several thousands of years of use, the clumsy core implement was discarded in favor of better implements made from flakes. Some of these were called "points." They were smaller, still oval in shape, edged on each side. The edges were further improved by "retouching." That means that after making an edge by striking off flakes, the Mousterian craftsman used a small tool to force tiny flakes from the margins by pressure. This made the entire implement thinner and so sharper.

Scrapers were made in special shapes evidently planned for special purposes. Man had begun to devise implements for use in different tasks. Other substances were added to the stock of flint and considered suitable for manufacturing purposes. It is quite probable that some of these had been in use earlier, but the students of cultures, like their associates in other sciences, need actual proof. So they were delighted to find in one of the very early

143

Mousterian industries at Clacton, England, a wooden spear.

During the Mousterian period bone is frequently used for many purposes. One of the most used pieces is called an "anvil." It does not greatly suggest an anvil except that it served—as the cuts on it testify—to support an implement in the process of manufacture. It is more like a small bone pad than an anvil. Bone splinters and split teeth were also used for the smaller "points" which were quite probably used as awls. Bone was also used for scrapers probably quite as often as flint.

For the first time a hammer-stone, definitely planned for such use, was found. Certainly these *must* have been in use earlier. No other implement could have been used in striking off the flakes from the cores. But at last, among Mousterian deposits, hammer-stones really take their place.

It is not strange that there should be variations of manufactures as there were variations in the skeletons of the Neandertals. We Americans, all living in the twentieth century, still have groups

144

among ourselves who manufacture articles planned for their own special needs. We do not find it strange that the Americans shut in the more simple world of the Kentucky Mountains make special blankets, while the New Englanders, forced by the closeness of their contacts with the whole eastern coast of the northern United States, have developed a general type of mill-made coverings which can be sold to many people.

When you think that such specialization can develop in three centuries it does not seem strange that people scattered over a greater space should develop special forms of their only manufacture— flint tools—during seventy centuries. Like the similarities in the skeletons of the Neandertals, the various cultures scattered over Europe, Asia, and Africa have enough likenesses to show us that they are the records of a great race once living throughout most of the world.

13

MANNERS AND CUSTOMS OF THE NEANDERTALS

BECAUSE the rock shelters were a much better place to preserve skeletons than the open camps had been, we know more of these people who lived during the cold centuries than we do of the Neandertals of the warm years. But there is a special reason why the caves tell us so much of the people they sheltered. Men had begun, deliberately, to bury their dead.

When this is done we not only gain an idea of the physical appearance of the people buried, but by studying the ways and means used in the burials we reach some idea of the thought which was behind the act. Of course this is partly guess work based on similar customs of primitive people living today; but it is probably close to the truth.

That Neandertals had begun to inter their dead and not leave them to the destruction of beasts and weather looks as if they might have had some hazy idea that there might be a future existence. Interment certainly argues respect for the departed. It has a ceremonious appearance too. At La Chapelle-aux-Saints, the skeleton which has already been mentioned lay in a shallow grave running east and west. Around it had been placed well made implements of the Mousterian type, fragments of red ochre, and broken animal bones. Ochre is a clay of the kind used in making porcelain which has been deeply colored by iron. From the position of these bones it seems that the dead must have been provided with implements and food to take into a spirit world.

At the rock shelter of Le Moustier where so much had been found a burial was discovered as late as 1908. Because by that time scientists had come to realize how important it was to find out all that could be known, geologically, physically, and psychologically, of primitive man, a large group of scientists from many countries gathered to see this grave opened. They found that the burial was that of a boy of perhaps sixteen—to judge from the condition of the bones and teeth. Near his right hand was an ax of Acheulian manufacture, but other implements of Mousterian workmanship were in the cave. The charred bones of one of the oxen which the Romans were to exterminate thousands of years later were also found in the grave. The boy's face had been turned downward and a pillow of stones arranged under the head. The entire body had been placed so that it lay on its right side.

The contents of a cave burial found at Krapina, Croatia, gave a grim idea of what life in Mousterian times had been. Charred bones were there also but they were the bones of human beings, men, women, and children. Some scientists have felt that they indicated cannibalistic customs such as Peking Man may have practiced. Others consider it a sacrificial burial. Some think that it may be the result of some desperate local famine. Perhaps when the animals fled from the cold that the humans were

braving, the inhabitants were driven to cannibal-
ism or to human sacrifice, as men were before and
have been since. As we have said many times, it is
only one instance and general conclusions cannot
be drawn from a single circumstance of any kind.
It happens that the burial at Krapina was a famous
one discussed in almost every book on primitive
man. For this reason it has seemed best to describe
it and give all the guesses made about it.

The red ochre which was found in the cave at
La Chapelle-aux-Saints forms the basis of speculation about another possible custom. We have more
ground for speculation because ochre was found at
other caves and in some camps. Some of the
scrapers are stained and so show that they must
have been used to scrape flakes from the chunks of
ore and probably to reduce the scraps to powder.
Color—at least this color—must have been ad-
mired since they thought it worth while to make
sure that some of it was left with those who no
longer needed it in this world but might need it
somewhere else. The use suggested to us by the

men still living in a primitive manner is painting the body. Perhaps that is what the Mousterians did. So far no caves in which Mousterian burials have been made have showed any trace of paintings, sculptures, or colored stones for which red was used.

Certain of the bone and quartz tools suggest that the Mousterians used skins for coverings. Some of the scrapers must have been used in dressing skins and the knives in removing and trimming the hides. Since no implement suggesting an awl or rude needle has been discovered, it seems likely that a single skin was used. Perhaps this was worn, as the natives of Tierra del Fuego wear their coverings today, on the side of the body nearest the wind.

There is no doubt but that the Mousterians had plenty of skins. The bones of game are exceedingly numerous in the rock shelters. Some of these belonged to big game—elephants, rhinoceroses, the ox (urus) already mentioned, some large deer which became extinct a little later. Of course there was the ever present hyena. There were wolves, a

NEANDERTAL CAVE SCENE. NOTE WOODEN SPEAR
AND MAN MAKING FLINT.

cave bear, and a number of small rodents such as marmots and a special chipmunk. Since the large game was much too large to have fallen to any attacking group, we think that Neandertal Man, like his predecessors, must have used pitfalls.

The game drifted southward as the glaciers advanced for the fourth time. This fourth advance was not so severe as the others and, as had happened before, many animals lingered on in a colder climate, adapting themselves for such a life. The Mousterians lingered too for thousands of years. Then they seem to vanish. Their rock shelters and caverns hold no more records. Some force greater than the cold they had defied so long must have forced them to leave the life to which they were so accustomed. Such a force might have been the invasion of a superior race. If that had happened, the victors might have left little of the people they conquered. And this is what we believe happened.

14

THE GRIMALDI RACE — STRANGERS IN EUROPE

AFTER the apparent disappearance of the Neandertal Race the history of man in Europe reads in a very modern manner. It is a series of invasions resulting in the establishment of the invader and the extinction or absorption of the native. If this sounds modern, so were those who enacted it for they, like ourselves, were *Homo sapiens*—Man of Thought.

While the ice had been advancing in Europe, Africa had enjoyed a comfortable climate. The frozen moisture which fell as snow in the north reached Africa in the shape of rain. What is now arid country was then fertile. Grass was plentiful; streams were full; game, driven south by the cold, was abundant. As European ice began to melt many animals started northward and it seems probable that men followed after the retreating game. Both would have used the land-bridges across the Mediterranean.

It is equally certain that some of the animals returned, not from Africa, but from Asia. It is equally possible that men followed these migrations. The route from the Yellow River to England was still open and Asia as well as Africa can show tools of various culture stages to prove that man must have lived on the plains, valleys, and low hills for many thousands of years. Scientists are still weighing the pros and cons of these returns and invasions. No definite decision has been reached. We can only accept the present conclusions held by the most careful students.

In Africa and in Asia many stages of developing cultures have been found. These range from the very early to those contemporaneous with the Mousterian culture which was itself present in Africa. The particular proof used in tracing man's route from Africa is a series of small implements.

These were first found in Tunisia and since that was anciently called Capsa this industry or culture is called Capsian. Its typical implement is a flint knife, small and retouched so that the edge is on one side only. Such knives are found in Spain, the logical place if their owners traveled from Africa.

In France the earliest implements which are believed to have been evolved from this Capsian style were first found in the same deposit as the Mousterian implements. This seems to indicate that the two manufacturers were living side by side for a little while. Then later the intruding culture develops and the skeletons of its makers are found carefully buried while there is no trace of the Neandertals.

That Neandertal Man perished completely is an idea which many scientists oppose. They seem to find traces of the Neandertal strain in skulls clearly belonging to a later period. This is a difficult point and "not proved" seems to be the best verdict. However, there is evidence—abundant evidence— that not all the intruders were of the same type.

156

There seem to be two or three distinct kinds of people so far as their skeletons show. Unfortunately several of these peoples, who are usually spoken of as races, are only known from two or three skeletons. These skeletons cannot be regarded as slightly changed forms of one great race as was the case with the Neandertals, but they are too few to give many hints of their origins or their forms of evolutionary change.

Many of these races are scattered over parts of Europe where the Neandertals had lived. They are found in Moravia, Bohemia, the Caucasus, and on the Volga. All of these localities suggest that the men living there were migrating or had migrated from Asia. But the small race which roused the greatest attention for its strangeness was found on the shores of the Mediterranean. In the tiny principality of Monaco there are nine caves called the Grottes de Grimaldi or Grimaldi Caves. These have now been much altered by land-slips for they are on the face of the cliffs. In 1901 two skeletons, one a boy's and the other a young woman's, were found in one of these caves.

Their burial was extremely interesting for much pains had evidently been taken. The skeletons were close together. The legs were bent upward at the knees and the woman's arms had been drawn up under her chin. The boy's right arm was bent but his left lay straight along his side. A shallow pit had been dug for the boy's head to rest in and a flagstone, supported by two uprights, protected both skulls. Flint knives and a scraper were found in the tomb and near the woman's right wrist were enough pierced snail shells to have formed a bracelet. The fact that the skeletons were buried together and that the woman was much older than the boy has suggested that they were mother and son. But that of course is only a guess.

The skeletons themselves give us a clear idea of the physical appearance of these people. They were comparatively short. The boy, perhaps fourteen or fifteen, is barely five feet tall. The woman, fully grown, older than the boy but not really old, is five feet two inches in height. The legs of both are long in comparison to their total height and their upper arms are long in comparison to the lower. The skulls are longer than wide. The teeth are large and so set that the lower jaw, which has a retreating chin, seems to protrude slightly.

Now all these peculiarities are characteristic of the negroid races, and originally the Grimaldi race was believed to be Negro but that idea made a lot of trouble. Indeed the Grimaldi race was quite as bothersome as Piltdown Man. Of course there were two skeletons but two skeletons are almost as insufficient evidence in describing a whole race of people as a piece of skull is in deciding about one individual. Moreover if these people were Negroes, they represented a distinct race which had no beginning.

After a while certain anthropologists suggested that these two skeletons had proportions from which the next intruders might have developed. These intruders were the Cro-Magnons. At first this was scoffed at, but quite recently two English anatomists, each working independently, have reached this conclusion—the Grimaldi skeletons are early members of the Cro-Magnon people who are found in Europe only a little later.

There are some students who claim the Grimaldi skeletons as migrants from Africa and find extra evidence in certain crude figures carved about this period. Those statuettes do resemble those made by certain African races living today. But this is very inconclusive evidence. Two very different peoples living under quite different conditions may produce objects which look alike just as they may produce articles which are unlike.

No more has been discovered about these two strangers, but very much more has been discovered about the people who lived in Europe only a very little later. These newcomers were so interesting as to quite overshadow the Grimaldi pair who may or may not have been representatives of their immediate ancestors.

15

THE CRO-MAGNONS—
INVADERS WITH IDEAS

THE race which seems to have invaded Europe was the famous Cro-Magnon race and if, after nearly seventy years of study, these people appear a little less amazing physically than they did when first discovered, nothing is likely to dim their lasting renown.

The first discovery of these people was made in 1868 when a railroad was being built through the little village of Les Eyzies in the Dordogne section of France. The tracks were to cross the highroad and at this junction was a large heap of mixed rock and earth, the accumulation of many hundreds of years, which had dropped as the cliff above wore away. Part of this was cleared away for the railroad and a little later more was carried off for road-mending. In doing this one of the old rock shelters was discovered. In the native patois this was dubbed Cro-Magnon, the great hole.

In moving the road material the two local contractors discovered a great number of animal bones and flints which they recognized as primitive weapons. Fortunately—and most unusually—they recognized that they had made a discovery which needed expert opinion. A few days later in the presence of witnesses two skulls and some skeletal fragments were exhumed. Then a trained archaeologist arrived on the scene and proceeded to uncover the rest of the skeletons with care.

He found that this rock shelter had been in use for centuries. One hearth had been built upon the other. This means that new fires were kindled where old fires had burned, after those who lighted the earlier ones had vanished for so long that rubbish dropping from the rocks above and dust blown by the wind had completely obliterated all traces of the earlier hearths. Remains of four skeletons were discovered. Since then many other skeletons

162

have been found in various parts of Europe including England. Africa has yielded some remains and it is possible that traces have been found in Asia.

The first impression of these people was based on the skeletons from Cro-Magnon and some skeletons found in the Grotte des Enfants in a layer above the two Grimaldi skeletons. In this cave fourteen individuals had been buried. These were not all found at the same time but by excavations which took nearly twelve years. As was the case with the Neandertals, all the Cro-Magnon skeletons show that they belonged to a race of people who must have lived in local groups which had individual differences from the general type of the race.

The men were tall, some being six feet, which is a marked change from the short stature of the earlier peoples. Originally it was supposed that all Cro-Magnons were tall but time produced proof that there was great variety in their height. Since the tallest men have been found buried together, it has been suggested that those burials may have been of a family or clan and so emphasized family peculiarities. Of course that is a mere guess. It is no guess, however, that the average height of all the men is greater than that of their predecessors. Skeletons of very few women have been found but these are much shorter than the men.

For the most part the face, like the height, is a sharp contrast to the earlier races. Only very few have heavy brow-ridges. Most individuals have as little as you or I. The face is broad but the forehead is vertical and the head is higher from ear to crown than those of earlier men. The growth of bone evidently took place along the sutures (joints in the bone) on the top of the skull as it does now. This means that those sutures closed much later than the ones along the side of the skull over which the jaw muscles fastened. Chewing rough and raw food would account for this. The exercise of the jaws developed the muscles early and consequently the bone on which they were anchored had to harden earlier than bone where no muscles fastened.

CRO-MAGNON MAN.

Courtesy of Dr. J. H. McGregor

The need of strong bone for muscle anchorage also probably accounts for the wide cheek-bones which made the face broad. And at last man had attained a really prominent chin. After nine hundred centuries he had ceased to be the Chinless Wonder.

He had also achieved a prominent nose and a good one after thousands of years. But he had achieved a great deal more. With the arrival of the Cro-Magnons we herald the arrival of men of our own kind—*Homo sapiens*. To the scientist the skeleton of Cro-Magnon Man, although it had come a long way from the beginnings of the Java Ape-man, shows that it was not yet quite that of the *Homo sapiens* Linnaeus had in mind as the type of man. To us these differences are invisible and we can think of the individuals of the Cro-Magnon and succeeding races as varying from each other only as living men differ today.

There is a great deal of material for comparison in the Cro-Magnons. The careful burials are those of individuals of various ages. One skeleton, found at Cro-Magnon, was that of an old man—quite

167

rare in these early people. He had broken his thigh when a grown man and nature had healed the bone before he died. The skeletons of two children were found in the Grotte des Enfants in 1874 and 1875, and under them an old woman had been buried. In 1892 in the Barma Grande, one of the larger Grimaldi caves, a triple burial was found. The skeleton of a tall man lay nearest the entrance. A young woman's bones came next and farthest from the entrance lay the skeleton of a boy of about fifteen.

All in all a far greater number of skeletons has been found than was left by any other race. Like their predecessors', Cro-Magnon skeletons are spread over the great stretch of territory where they lived.

One of the most interesting things about these graves is that almost all contain some coloring matter. For the most part this is red ochre, a natural mixture of clay and iron, but there are other minerals such as hematite, one of the ores of iron. Cro-Magnons may have used this color to ornament their bodies since red may have symbolized to them the blood and so life and vigor and hardihood. It may have been put into the grave so that, in some other existence, life might be strong.

Ornaments are also found in the graves. There are pierced snail shells and stag's teeth which have been drilled for the thongs which moldered away many thousands of years ago. Some of these were used for armlets and anklets since they lie on the arms and about the ankles of the skeletons. One individual must have worn a head-dress of some kind, for two hundred perforated snail shells lay about a skull found in the Grimaldi caves.

In 1852 a cave was discovered at Aurignac in the Haute-Garonne department of France. No one had known that a cave existed, for falling debris had hidden it for hundreds of years. When it was opened eighteen skeletons were found and a kindly mayor, believing them modern men and victims of an accident, ordered them given Christian burial. As a matter of fact these skeletons were those of Neolithic men (thousands of years later than the

Cro-Magnons) who had been buried in a cave already old. A French archaeologist, attracted by a report of the discovery, arrived on the scene and began a scientific excavation. Under the level in which the Neolithic skeletons had been buried was another stratum which showed that man had occupied—and had left—the cave before the Neolithic period. In this sub-stratum were found the Cro-Magnon flint implements which have been given the cultural name of the cave, Aurignacian. Since that first discovery, implements of the same type have been found over many parts of Europe. Some have been found in Africa.

It is important to understand about the names of different cultures and the men who made them. When a race lives thousands of years, as the Neandertals did, they improve their manufactures as they progress in time. The Neandertals—all that great scattered group of people—began by making the Acheulian type of flints and then developed the Mousterian type and a dozen smaller varieties which we have not named.

170

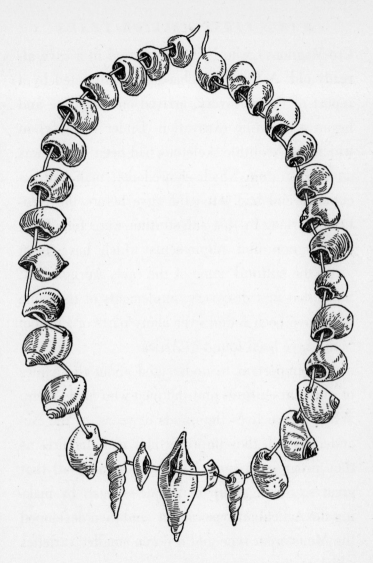

NECKLACE OF SHELLS FROM THE CAVE OF CRO-MAGNON.

With the arrival of the Cro-Magnons we are dealing with men of our own kind, *Homo sapiens*. They have produced not one but hundreds of types of flints and arts. Cultures are named from the place where they are found first or at their best. The fossils of men are named either from the place where they are found or from some striking characteristic. So we have two sets of names contemporaneous in time, one standing for man and the other for his works. The name of the culture is often transferred to the people. The Neandertals who made Mousterian flints are often called the Mousterians. So the Cro-Magnons who made the flints found at Aurignac are usually called Aurignacians.

These Aurignacians had found a better method of striking flakes from the rough nodule or nucleus so that they were longer and thinner. With a little imagination they could be thought of as rather like a small knife blade. After these were made, the margin was chipped on one face (side) only so that the edge was thinner and consequently sharper. This was the general fashion of working and, having made this improvement, the craftsmen went on to improve the shapes of the weapons and tools.

In one case they retouched the right-hand edge only. This left the left dull like the back of a knife blade. It was for this reason it was done. The implement is a knife or a scraper which was held in the right hand with the right forefinger extended along the dull edge so that the weight of the hand could be brought down on the blade without injury. This knife was itself not new but the development of the edge was.

Some previously existing implements were never altered by the Aurignacians. Such tools were hammer-stones, anvils, side-scrapers, and a few others, but some of the new inventions were most interesting. One of the strangest weapons produced was made toward the end of Aurignacian times. It is called a strangled point or sometimes a strangulated point. In appearance it is rather like a lance point choked in the middle. Each edge is notched with quite even chipping. It was probably a side-scraper or a most primitive drawknife.

Among the flints is one which, even if not so much a worked tool as the scrapers, knives, and engraving tools, is perhaps the most exciting implement found. We have often heard that pioneers depended upon flints to light their fires but we usually think of those pioneers as only a century or two ahead of us. Here were pioneers more than a hundred centuries ahead of us and they used flint lighters too. Of course, from the numbers of campfires found and from the fact that some were in caves and some in the open just as their makers had wished, archaeologists were pretty sure that man had learned to light his fires where he willed. Still, archaeologists are as bad as paleontologists. They say, "Show me the tool." So here is the tool and we can *prove* that man, after more than nine hundred thousand years, struck flint against flint when he wished to kindle a blaze. Probably flint workers for centuries had seen the sparks fly as they flaked flints and at last they had reached the

175

point of utilizing the sparks. Nearly twenty thousand years ago they lighted fires almost at will.

One of the new tools was used for engraving and was called a burin. This rough ancestor of the etcher's "point" and the engraver's tool served these craftsmen well as we shall see.

A new type of lance point also claims our attention. This was a long, oval point with a slit in the base. Here was a real bit of invention. Into the slot a lance haft could be slipped and so a heavier weapon could be used which would not be lost if its point were blunted or broken. One haft only could be carried and a crude pouch of skin would hold several points when hunting. These lance points are not flint implements. Very rarely they were shaped from ivory, sometimes from reindeer horn, but the usual material was bone.

This new medium, indeed, was the one used for many new tools. Awls were made from it. So were needles. At last man could put two skins together and protect himself from a climate which made protection very necessary. However, do not picture

176

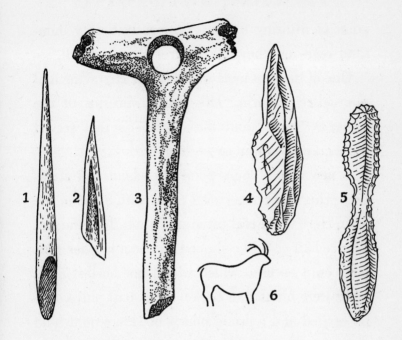

AURIGNACIAN IMPLEMENTS.

1. DART POINT OF BONE
2. AWL FROM BONE SPLINTER
3. LANCE SHAFT STRAIGHTENER (BATON DE COM-
   MANDEMENT)
4. BURIN OR ENGRAVING TOOL
5. NOTCHED SIDESCRAPER
6. CAVE DRAWING

Courtesy of Dr. Nelson and the American Museum of Natural History

Cro-Magnon man clothed like an Indian; he probably contented himself with a rude poncho or blanket-robe. But he at least produced toggles which may have helped hold it together.

One striking implement was invented in this age and reached its real importance a few centuries later. This has been called the "bâton de commandement" because it was supposed that it represented some insignia of office—was the chief's ranking sign. Now we know that it served a much more utilitarian purpose. Comparison with tools still in use by primitive men has showed that it probably served as a gauge for bent lance-shafts. Usually this implement was made from a reindeer antler but other bone could be used provided the top portion was at an angle to the shaft. At the point where the angle came—usually a little wider than the rest of the tool—a round hole was laboriously worked out. Through this hole a lance shaft would be passed. When the shaft stuck it was pared down. There was another possible use for this baton. It might have straightened kinked and hardened rawhides used for thongs. Slowly pulled through the hole, worked backward and forward until soft enough to pass, a thong, hardened beyond use, would be supple again.

This use of bone is the outstanding change in the Aurignacian manufacture. Bone was beginning to play an even larger part than flint. The Aurignacian artisan worked it even better than the older, less yielding material. If it was less durable than stone, it was also more easily adjusted for new uses and more quickly worked and quite as easily found. The Cro-Magnons chose it not only for use but for purposes not purely utilitarian.

16

THE ART OF THE AURIGNACIANS

THE difference between the utilitarian and the ornamental shows us the great advance made by the Cro-Magnons. Earlier human beings had been content just to live—so far as we can judge. Now a race of people appeared, living at a time when the cold must have made existence almost unendurable, who yet found in themselves something unconnected with the thoughts of enough food and enough fire.

Perhaps it is not correct to say that the earlier people had shown *no* indications that their thoughts strayed beyond the necessities of every day. The Mousterians, you remember, at least had some artistic instincts. Pierced snail shells were found buried with their dead and those shells were certainly used for ornament. But that was as far as their artistic sense seemed to go. Yet the Mousterians had at their command the same material from which to fashion attempts toward beauty.

Like the Mousterians or like primitive people of much later time, the first efforts of the Aurignacians were personal ornaments. In their burials, besides pierced shells, beads pierced for stringing are found. Ivory beads, occasionally used, were as rare then as pearls are now, but beads of bone are fairly common. There were other necklaces. The most elaborate used stag's teeth for slides with strands of fish vertebrae and snail shells between. There were simpler ornaments too. Pierced teeth—wolves', elks', bears', and human— were clearly intended to hang as pendants. So far as we can tell from the burials, both men and women wore such ornaments. To such minds as we judge the Aurignacians possessed, those pierced teeth may have served as <u>amulets</u> rather than as ornaments. What was more natural than that a hunter, wishing to possess the slyness and fierceness of a wolf or the strength of a cave bear, should have hung a tooth of the animal round his neck so that some of the spirit, clinging around the object, might find its way into his own heart?

EARLY AURIGNACIAN DRAWINGS. PRIMITIVE PAINTED OUTLINES FROM THE CAVERN WALLS OF FONT-DE-GAUME.

It was not unlikely that this desire to make men more successful hunters had a part in producing the art for which the Cro-Magnons are still celebrated—their mural paintings in caves. These were not, as you might naturally suppose, in the caves where men lived. These home caves are easily identifed by the kitchen refuse found on the cave floors. The best mural paintings are in caves not used for living and caves which are, and must have been, difficult to reach. Many are dark. Artificial

MAMMOTH PAINTED IN RED OCHRE IN THE CAVERN OF PINDAL. (AFTER BREUIL.)

light of some kind must have been used at the time when the painting was done.

So well did darkness conceal these paintings that the first fresco was discovered by accident. In 1879 a Spanish archaeologist, Sautuola, inspired by the display of prehistoric handiwork exhibited

184

at the Paris Exposition of 1878, set out to search
the Spanish caves. His little daughter accompanied

**STAG ENGRAVED ON CEILING IN CAVERN OF ALTA-
MIRA.**

him and, bored or inquisitive, looked up to the
cave roof instead of down to the floor where cleavers and lance heads might be found. What she saw
in the uncertain candlelight made her exclaim

185

with surprise. Her father, coming to find the cause for her exclamation, looked upward also and was amazed.

Well he might have been, for he had found one of the finest bits of prehistoric mural in Europe. His discovery was not credited. No one doubted its beauty or fine workmanship but they did doubt that it was the work of primitive man. It was not until twenty years later that evidence in the French caverns supported the contention that the prehistoric population of Spain had produced some excellent artists.

By that time it had occurred to some scientists to compare the bones of the fossil bison and particularly their horns with the bison pictured on the cave walls. What had been taken for a modern animal—a few wild bison were still alive in hunting preserves—was a very different animal. The painted creature and the fossil bones were the same beast. So the painting must have been done at a time when the fossil bison was alive to sit for his portrait.

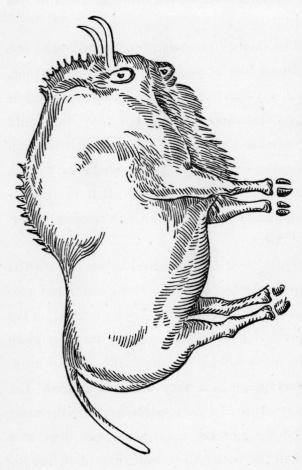

BISON PAINTED IN FOUR COLORS ON CEILING OF CAVERN OF ALTAMIRA. (AFTER BREUIL.)

The fresco Sautuola found really belonged to a later period than the Aurignacian. The artists who had made it had superior abilities to the Cro-Magnons. But the first artists, even if their style was less finished, deserve all the credit of pioneers as well as credit of being good artists. Though they never used so fine a technique as that in Altamira (Sautuola's cave), the Cro-Magnon artists were able and, as was the case with their flints, their art improved with time.

At first they engraved or cut their outlines. That means that with their flint engravers or burins they laboriously cut lines in the rocky walls of the caves they chose to beautify. They were good outlines if crude compared with those made later. The animals produced are easily recognizable and lifelike in attitude if a little stiff. Into these outlines and sometimes over the entire animal the Aurignacian artist smeared color. This was red (from iron), ochre (which we found earlier), and black (carbon from the burned wood of the fires). All were mixed with fat tried from animals. The emptied hollows of marrow bones were man's first paint tubes.

How can we be sure just when the artists made the murals? The prehistoric archaeologist has vari-

AURIGNACIAN PAINTING OF WOOLLY RHINOCEROS.

ous methods of determining the age of cave painting. Perhaps the cave entrance was covered with a heap of debris containing bones of animals belonging to Aurignacian time. Then the paintings were made before the heap accumulated. Perhaps a piece of the fresco itself has fallen to the floor and been buried. Then the painting from which it fell is at least as old as the flints and bones into which it tumbled. Perhaps the painting has been partly

190

buried in a deposit containing flint knives of early Aurignacian pattern. Then the wall was already ornamented when that deposit began to accumulate. Since it has been fairly easy to determine the age of the implements, they help date the frescoes. The last check is the general style of the painting itself which archaeologists recognize as easily as we recognize the style of artists who painted on canvas.

The pictures of the animals themselves tell something about the age in which they were produced. The bones of animals used for food and found with the cast-off implements of a race are also found in deposits where nature and not man left them. That is a second general check. If paleontologist and geologist say "Fourth Interglacial" to nature's heaps and the archaeologist says "Cro-Magnon" to man's refuse piles, each has said the same thing in his own language.

It is thought that the Mousterians may have begun another kind of art by slightly altering stones already shaped by nature. This is not yet proved

191

to the archaeologists' satisfaction, but if we accept it as true we do have a natural bridge from the art-less Neandertals to the few statuettes belong-

AURIGNACIAN ENGRAVING OF MAMMOTH.

ing to the Aurignacian era. We have all, at some time in our younger days, picked up a stone which looked like some animal, nut, or root. To take that stone and give it a touch here and there to increase that resemblance is an easy matter for a flint worker. It is so that we think the early Aurignacians may have begun their careers as sculptors.

By the time they had many hundreds of years' experience behind them, they had greatly improved. Cro-Magnon man, like ourselves, had the

HEAD CARVED IN IVORY BY AURIGNACIAN ARTIST.

type of brain capable of learning from experience. Certainly the engravings of animals are life-like in the extreme, but when it came to human figures the artists were not so successful. Under the strain of effort they seem to have adopted a style now much in vogue—that of conventionalizing or stylizing what could not be portrayed satisfactorily in a realistic manner. In this way human figures were

193

drawn, or at least that is an explanation. Faces are almost blank and a general style of figure was used.

Curiously enough, this race of advanced Stone Age men seems to have had no idea of creating mythical characters such as our Indians and many primitive races have imagined and given shape. Among pictures and sculptures none is thought to represent gods. Yet, since the cave paintings were in places little seen, they must have been put there for some very special reason. A painting a few thousand years nearer our day will give us the key when we come to its creation.

17

SOLUTREANS — FLINT WORK-ERS AND STONE AGE IMMIGRANTS

ONLY a little later than the time when the Cro-Magnons were making their flints and decorating their caverns, another race lived in the territory the earlier flint makers had occupied. Like their predecessors, these men too were true *Homo sapiens* and it is unnecessary to devote much time to a description of their physical appearance. The living human who most suggests them is the Eskimo and whether he is or is not a *very* distant living descendant is one of the arguments in the history of man.

The skeletons of these people are very little help in determining to what variety of *Homo sapiens* they belonged. It takes hundreds of measurements

195

to allow a physical anthropologist (a man interested in the bodily build of peoples) to determine any general tendency of a people to this or that length of arm or leg. Only where a whole race has very definite characteristics is a skeleton easily placed. These fossil men are too few to make so many measurements possible. So we trace their history by their flints and not their fossils.

The more crudely made flints, of a kind which we will very shortly describe in detail, are found in the east of Europe. The more carefully made ones are found in the western part of the continent. So we deduce that these new people came from Asia and worked their way westward probably following great herds of game. Because the flints of the earlier type are few in number and mingled with a great number of Aurignacian weapons, we think that the vanguard of the tribes arrived first and settled among the Cro-Magnons. They learned enough of the Aurignacian methods (practiced by the Cro-Magnons) to improve their weapon-making and passed on this knowledge to the bulk of their people

196

who arrived later.

When these newcomers arrived in great numbers in central France, they apparently drove away the Aurignacians. The reason for thinking this is that in the great open air camp, where a few new weapons had been found with many Aurignacian flints, there are now found many of the new implements and only a very few of those which the Aurignacians had worked.

This camp was made on the south side of a great outcrop of limestone which kept off the colder, northern winds and was situated near the village of Solutré near the Saône river in south-central France. It must have been the camp site of a great number of people for it covers more than two acres and has innumerable hearths where great campfires once burned. The flints found among these long dead ashes have been given the name of the camp—Solutrean. So, to distinguish them from other members of the great *Homo sapiens* division of primates, their makers have been called Solutreans.

This great camp site was discovered in 1866. One of the fires must have been over fourteen feet long, for the slabs on which the ashes rested meas-

SITE OF ANCIENT CAMP OF SOLUTREANS NEAR THE PRESENT VILLAGE OF SOLUTRE, FRANCE. RICH DISCOVERIES HAVE BEEN MADE HERE.

ure that length. With the ashes are charred bones of animals telling of the great feasts held there. There are stag, cattle, and mammoth bones but by far the greater number are those of reindeer. At the time it was found Solutré was the largest camp of primitive men ever unearthed. About twenty years ago an almost equally large camp which had been inhabited by Solutrean hunters was found at Prědmost, Moravia. The hunters in this camp apparently had followed the mammoth, for an almost incredible number of bones and tusks were found there.

In earlier Solutrean stations, as we said, the flints were made in much the same style as those of the Aurignacians. After a time the newer arrivals developed their own technique and their own style of implements. Their technique consisted first in their ability to strike off flakes and then in their manner of finishing the weapons. They struck off flakes which, compared with earlier products, were very long and thin. Then using another smaller tool they chipped each face all over by forcing out tiny chips through pressure (pressure chipping). The result has been called a "laurel-leaf point" for the obvious reason that its shape suggests a laurel leaf. This was used, probably, both as a spear point and as a knife. Smaller flakes, treated in the same

199

manner, have been named "willow-leaf points" and were probably used in the same way.

In addition to these weapons made by a new method the Solutreans also invented a lance point or arrow fabricated in still another manner. This too was made from a flake but was pressure chipped on one face only. One such point had a shoulder or barb on one edge and a second type had a long stem from which it takes its name of "stemmed point."

In 1873 at Volgu in the Loire section of France, fourteen of the laurel-leaf points were found in what seemed a cache. These points are far finer than any others discovered and one at least was covered with red ochre. All were so fine that it has been supposed they were intended, since they are much too fragile for use, as a votive offering. Whether the spot in which they were found was a sacred spot in the mythology of this long-vanished people or whether, having placed them for safe-keeping, their owner never returned to take part in some votive service we shall never know.

200

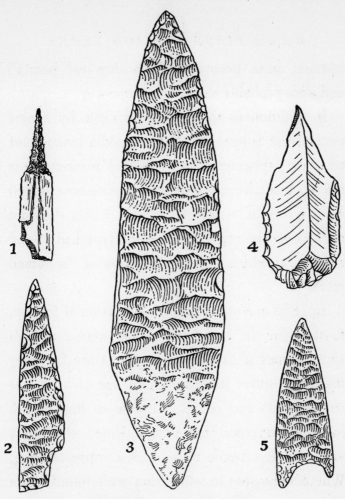

SOLUTREAN IMPLEMENTS.

1. BURIN OR BORER

2. LANCE POINT

3. KNIFE OR SPEAR POINT—LAUREL LEAF TYPE

4. COMBINATION ENDSCRAPER OR BURIN

5. ARROW POINT

Courtesy of Dr. Nelson and the American Museum of Natural History

The Solutreans did use bone, but compared with the Aurignacians they were poor artificers in that material. It seems strange that such skilled workers in flint should have lost the magic touch for a

SOLUTREAN ORNAMENT. PENDANT OF IVORY.

more easily workable material. To each his own way, however, and the only bone tool the Solutreans made in any quantity was the pressure chipper which they used in finishing their famous flaked flint tools. They did use bone a little for ornament and they did engrave on it but scarcely with the finish of the Aurignacians.

They were also very good sculptors. The best example of Solutrean work was discovered at Le

Roc, Charente, France. Le Roc is a valley bounded by cliffs. In it was found a cave having a natural platform in front. Evidently the Solutreans had used this as a workshop, for it was quite heaped with flawed tools. There were also ashes and burned bone in heaps large enough to suggest that the Solutreans had occupied the place for a long time. At the back of this platform was a semicircle of blocks which had either fallen or been thrown from a ledge above. In order to continue the study of the platform, these blocks were moved and it was found that the sides on which they had fallen were covered with animal sculpture. When put in place on the ledge these sculptures made a frieze of moving creatures.

The experts believe that this frieze is the work of several artists. Each has his individual touch. All the animals are represented as walking and their attitudes show great power of observation as well as skill in execution. Two small horses, a musk-ox with lowered head charging a fleeing man, another short-legged horse, and two other horses follow each other across the rock ledge just as their makers left them perhaps fifteen thousand years ago. In the Field Museum of Chicago a reproduction has been made with actual casts and before it you can see one of the Solutreans, his covering of reindeer hide thrown aside, busy at the work finished so long ago.

These carved animals, as well as the charred bones at Solutré and other camps, give us a very clear idea of the game the Solutreans hunted. In their turn these animals indicate the climate in which they must have lived. So we know that the air was still cold and that the great camp-fires were a necessity as well as a protection. Yet the cold was less than in Aurignacian times or no great outdoor camp would ever have been established.

Indeed the glaciers were making their final retreat. Little by little, almost literally inch by inch, their southern edges drew northward. In the valleys the streams ran more freely while the mountain tops glistened under a warmer sun. The reindeer began to shift their ground but not sufficiently to check man's food supply. Reindeer were a staple for the next thousand years or so but the great massed herds thinned slightly in southwestern Europe and the ground grew darker with their numbers in the northern valleys.

It is suggested that as the reindeer herds withdrew the Solutreans followed; that this time their nomadic wanderings led them, after centuries passed, into the north. Some claim that the living Eskimo descends from these Stone Age people. This has not been proved; but what is proved beyond doubt is that after a few centuries more the Solutrean culture vanished from Europe.

18

THE LAST STAND OF UNPOLISHED STONE

THE tools, weapons, and ornaments of the Solutreans grow less as the deposits creep upward; their bones are no longer found. But a new culture takes the place of the old and indeed is found overlapping the last of the Solutrean records. Perhaps the Solutreans drifted northward where the glaciers wiped out traces of their later activities. Perhaps, for no known reason, they simply ceased to exist in their earlier camps.

Possibly the new race whose bones and implements are found came *from* the north, advancing ahead of the glaciers which were making a dying spurt at this time. The air of southern Europe was cold but, because the glaciers had really left the south, it was dry and not moist. So the glaciers *might* have wiped out traces both of the Solutreans' retreat and of the advance of another, slightly different people. The fact that the Mediterranean coasts of Europe show no early traces of an invading culture is a fact in support of this theory. Theory it must be however for there are not enough facts to prove it. Another theory—that these new-comers like the Solutreans descended from a stock which furnished ancestors for the Cro-Magnons also—has quite as much support in the physical build of the new people. The truth may be that they were slowly developing into a race while the Cro-Magnons and Solutreans dominated the world.

These new members of the *Homo sapiens* clan were not quite the same in appearance as the Solutreans. They were slightly taller as an average. Their faces were broad but their skulls were oval—longer from front to back than the measurement from side to side.

The first discovery of this race was made in 1862 when two French archaeologists were exploring

208

the Dordogne region of France. On the same side
of the river as the famous shelter, Le Moustier,
and a little way below it they opened up another
rock shelter. This, by its contents of worked flints
and skeletons, proved itself the tomb of a different
culture. The ruins of the once famous monastery of
La Madeleine were only a short distance from this
grotto so it received that name and the implements
found in it came to be called Magdalenian. Since
that first discovery, other caves and shelters have
been found in Spain, Hungary, and Switzerland
while France has shown many more.

The skeletons belonging to the Magdalenian period are not very numerous but fortunately they
represent men and women both young and old. A
few children's bones have also been found. Some
of these skeletons, if they were deliberately buried,
were so carelessly interred that only incomplete
collections of bones have been found. Some skeletons, covered with ochre, were laid at full length as
the Aurignacians interred their dead. A very few
were buried with the knees drawn up to the head

which was so bent that the entire back was curved. The hands were drawn up and around the skull. Such a posture suggests the constricted pose of the bodies in Peruvian mummy bundles but the Magdalenian bodies are not numerous enough to make it possible to say that this form of burial was deliberately practiced.

As more and more implements were found it became clear that the Magdalenians improved their technique with time. But time was not very long, for not more than five or six thousand years passed while these people were the most important inhabitants in Europe.

The most interesting thing about Magdalenian tool manufacture was the almost complete abandonment of flint. At first tools were fashioned in the Aurignacian style. Suddenly flint was abandoned. After thousands and thousands of years when flint had been the main stock of the craftsman it was no longer found suitable. When we think of the amazing fineness of the Solutrean workmanship, it almost seems that the Magdale-

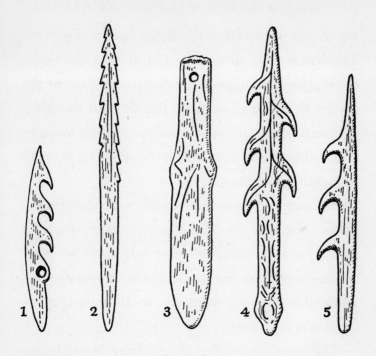

MAGDALENIAN IMPLEMENTS.

1. HARPOON POINT OF ANTLER
2. DART POINT OF BONE
3. ORNAMENTAL DAGGER OF BONE
4. HARPOON POINT OF ANTLER
5. ANOTHER HARPOON POINT

Courtesy of Dr. Nelson and the American Museum of Natural History

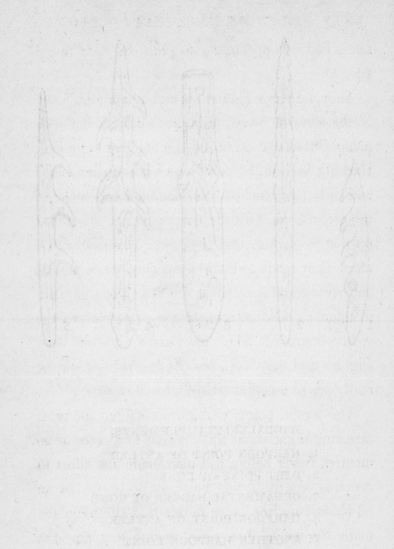

nians had no opportunity to profit by their methods.

They did retain hammer-stones and anvils. Some of the scrapers were the same although not well made. But at that point the Magdalenians stopped. Harking back to the point which the Aurignacians had only just reached, the Magdalenians took up the use of bone. This they improved and developed until it is obvious that they were superior craftsmen. They made awls, needles, pins, lance points, and straighteners of lance shafts (bâtons de commandement). But almost all these implements were vastly improved. The new awls or needles were slighter and they had eyes! At last skins could be really sewed together securely for garments.

The javelin points were numerous but the most arresting thing about them is that they were ornamented. Never before had man made any effort to decorate his utilitarian belongings. It was as an off-shoot from the lance points that the Magdalenians developed their most unique weapon—the barbed harpoon. That it is a member of the lance point family is clear but it developed quickly. First somewhat sharp, irregular notches were made on javelin points. Next these points were definitely notched on one side. The last step consisted in carving out points carefully spaced on both sides. The harpoon point was complete. Its development had been a definite piece of planned manufacture.

Equally striking was the artistic development of those horn or bone implements called bâtons de commandement. They too were commonplace implements, but under the hands of Magdalenian workmen they became decorative objects as well. Animals were etched on their handles. Sometimes, toward the end of the period, a row of beasts was carved on the long shanks. The upper part was carved as an animal head. No wonder archaeologists, who had no complete comparison at first, believed them to be chiefs' staffs—tokens of command.

Even more elaborate and often better adapted to ornamentation were the spear throwers found in Magdalenian deposits. This was a new weapon entirely, though today it is still in use among several peoples. Some of the animal forms are crude. But the later tools were finely finished. These dart-throwers were usually of bone; sometimes they were beautifully worked from ivory.

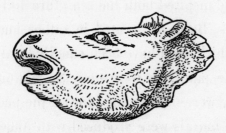

MAGDALENIAN SCULPTURE. HEAD OF HORSE CARVED ON REINDEER HORN. FOUND AT MAS D'AZIL.

This ability to produce really fine examples of animal sculpture was one of the outstanding points of the Magdalenian culture. That clay was used by sculptors then as it is today was discovered in 1912 when two bison beautifully modeled in clay were found in a cave in France. They were in an inner chamber of the cave and had been preserved because the clay had hardened without cracking—or

215

at least cracking to pieces. In the floor near them was the print of a human foot—made by a man bent on finishing his work or by a suppliant come to work magic through these life-like beasts.

It seems probable that the desire to work magic may have inspired both the sculpture and the wall paintings. Both are located in rather inaccessible places which must have been equally hard to reach when the paintings were new. So it would seem that they were not intended for all the people. Yet the cave murals were produced with difficulty and prepared with great care—there are few re-drawings among them. We must assume that they were deliberately placed in spots remote and dim today but infinitely more mysterious when only tried fat spluttered in stone lamps such as the Magdalenians have left in their caves.

Among the hordes of splendidly wrought animals which cover walls and ceilings in the caves of Spain and France the human figure holds small space. Procession after procession of mammoth, horse, reindeer, and bison adorn the walls. Only here

216

and there are figures clearly stylized in the act of hunting. These groups appear occasionally but on the wall of the Cave of the Three Brothers, at Ariège, there is a well-drawn figure of a man. He

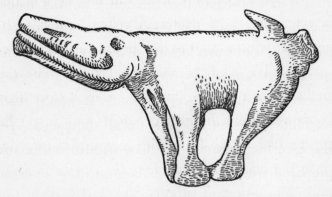

MAGDALENIAN DART-THROWER MADE OF REINDEER HORN.

wears a robe of reindeer skin and a mask, while antlers are fastened to his head. He so strongly suggests the witch-doctor or medicine-man that it seems impossible not to believe that he was represented as engaged in magic incantation over the beasts on the walls near him.

We can think of a magician coming into power

217

in some such fashion as this: Some hunter in a tribe was so successful that he gained a great reputation, and belief grew that he had some special way of securing power. This soon became belief that he had magic power and so he became a dealer in magic or a witch-doctor. A young hunter, wishing success, would go to him to ask for help in securing a large kill of animals. By this time the medicine-man would have begun to believe that his powers were the gifts of spirits who might be approached successfully with awe and ceremony.

So the magician would take the novice to some cave. As guide and suppliant walked farther and farther away from the entrance, the only light came from the flickering wick of moss floating in the fat-filled stone lamp held by the magician. That only seemed to make darkness visible as the draughts almost extinguished the flame and the shadows advanced and withdrew from the advancing men. Strange sounds filled the darkness. Sounds of moisture dripping from the roof and underground streams gurgling uncannily in their

218

hidden beds filled the novice's ears, and although in the light he would have known their meaning the darkness robbed them of reality. At last an inner-

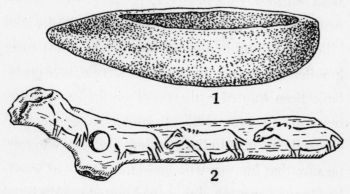

MAGDALENIAN IMPLEMENTS.

1. LAMP OF STONE
2. ARROW SHAFT STRAIGHTENER OR BATON DE COMMANDEMENT MADE OF ANTLER WITH HORSE ENGRAVINGS.

Courtesy of Dr. Nelson and the American Museum of Natural History

most room, known to the sorcerer, was reached. Perhaps there was a ritual dance in the shifting shadows, shadows so heavy that there was no sense of walls or roof. At the end the medicine-man lifted the lamp high and its uncertain flame brought to life the innumerable animals on walls and roof. The play of shadows seemed to make them move.

After such a ceremony the Magdalenian hunter went out to slay his beasts. Large ones, such as the mammoths, must have been trapped in pitfalls and killed by yelling hordes hurling spears and stones. Smaller creatures—bison, horses, reindeer—may have been hunted with spears or they may have been driven over cliffs or into a cul-de-sac and clubbed, as our Indians killed buffalo. We can be sure that hunters who had lance shafts of wood had long known the club—the knotted stock which is nature's ready-made weapon.

As the glaciers again took up their final retreat, the hunters may have wandered farther and farther in search of the game they liked best. The bones tell us that red deer, which was doubtless good eating, was beginning to replace the reindeer in the south. Yet the refuse piles of camps also show us that reindeer remained the great staple of food.

There must have been a slight change in hunting habits as the animals shifted and with that probable change there was certainly a change in the culture. The cave pictures, dated by the implements found above them, become less realistic and more stylized. Sometimes this stylization is a

HEADS OF CHAMOIS ENGRAVED ON FRAGMENT OF REINDEER HORN. (AFTER PIETTE.)

delightful success. When a whole herd of reindeer are depicted on an eight inch bone by a few living lines, the method deserves every praise. The strokes only suggest a mass of horns but so well that the entire herd seems to be pressing forward.

Conventionalization began to play a large part in the later Magdalenian art. Designs which are simply combinations of lines were engraved upon bone. Others suggest vines and some resemble sym-

221

bols. If these had a meaning we have not discovered it. It may be that they were only lines arranged to please their engravers. Probably the

FEMALE BISON PAINTED ON CEILING OF CAVERN AT
ALTAMIRA. (AFTER BREUIL.)

motifs of these line engravings were animal eyes, horns, or the figures of birds or fish.

Whatever the motifs which inspired these conventional symbols, the great art of the Magdalenians—the murals—suffered. Previously Magdalenian artists had achieved the great frescoes which adorn the caves of Altamira, Font-de-Gaume, and

222

a dozen smaller caverns. Artists of our time with better materials and lighting have made little improvement over the animal portraits and hunting scenes produced thousands of years ago. But their great day passed as the Magdalenians, conventionalizing their methods, used cruder technique in place of line and color.

This is especially noticeable in the cave paintings of Spain. Indeed the wall paintings, which date themselves as belonging to the close of this period, almost suggest that they are the work of a different people. They bear a curious resemblance to the Bushman work of Africa. Those scientists who see in the Grimaldi race the remnant of an African invasion feel equally sure that the Spanish paintings are related to another art and another continent.

This must stand as one of the many not proven theories so far as we know today. We can all agree, however, that the great period of Magdalenian art which reached its height in very few thousand years deteriorated even more quickly. An even greater change came within a few hundred years. A different art and a different set of implements were in use on the same ground which had been the site of man's endeavors for several hundred thousand years.

19

ADVANCING TIME AND CHANGED CULTURES

PERHAPS one thing which brought about a change in man's habits was the changed conditions under which he lived. The glaciers were seeking their final homes. Only the Scandinavian peninsula was ice-covered in part. Central Europe was much as it is now. The cold-loving reindeer were disappearing completely but the deer multiplied. These found splendid living in the dense forests of oak and birch. As the cold had lessened, these trees crept back, mingled with the pines, and began to replace them so that the forests were less gloomy. Those open stretches of sparse, cold-resistant vegetation, the tundras, were replaced by landscapes of bushes and trees. As the tundras vanished, the mammoths whose browsing grounds they had been vanished with them. The horse which had also lived there migrated to Asia.

The people who lived under these new conditions were probably descendants of the Magdalenians and probably also the last nomadic hunters to wander over Europe. The name Azilian, given to their culture, comes from the Mas d'Azil, a cave on the left bank of the Arise in the Ariège section of France. This river flows for a quarter of a mile through a great subterranean passage tunneled out of a limestone formation. Just before the mouth of this underground river bed opens, the grotto is located in the limestone. Its name is a local corruption of *Maison d'Asyle* which it was called when the grotto was supposed to have sheltered fleeing Huguenots.

The human bones found in it are scarcely distinguishable from those of men of earlier times or from later comers, but the implements and ornaments found in the Mas d'Azil are unique. The original discovery was made by Edouard Piette in 1887. By the side of the river as it passed through the natural tunnel, a highway had been built and from this highway Piette saw the Magdalenian deposits. Above these he found the layer with the distinctive implements and ornaments which has been given the name Azilian. Since then discoveries of Azilian age have been made as far north as Scotland, as far east as Russia, and as far west as Spain.

From these discoveries it has been established that the Azilians used a little flint worked in Aurignacian and Magdalenian fashion. The implements themselves were smaller and they were more crudely made. They included hammer-stones and anvils, rubbing-stones for smoothing edges of flints, scrapers, engraving tools, a stemmed point, and several other types which had long been in use.

The Azilians were not such competent bone workers as the Magdalenians but their most notable weapon was made from that substance. Perhaps the fact that deer, which had taken the place of the reindeer, was more difficult to hunt and so caught in smaller quantities made the supply of bone more limited than it had been for the Magdalenians. Whatever the cause, the Azilians produced harpoon points of staghorn which were crude in comparison with the Magdalenian harpoons. Azilian harpoons were about four inches long, flat and rather broad, and the base had a hole pierced through the horn. The Azilians also produced some new tools such as an adze of flint hafted in an antler and one made of antler hafted in the same fashion.

As implement makers they cannot be considered good workers, and their attempts at art were unusual rather than beautiful. Painted pebbles are an interesting example. Pebbles had been used before for ornaments. The Magdalenians had pierced smooth pebbles—perhaps after rubbing them a little smoother. The Azilian pebbles, however, were quite different. Flat, smoothly worn pebbles were chosen from the beds of streams and were not pierced but painted. Red ochre, probably mixed with fat, was painted on them in designs so stylized that they are usually called symbols.

Some of these signs suggest writing and Piette, their discoverer, was sure that they were actually used in this way. It would be delightful to think that at least twelve of these symbols had passed down into classical Latin but we cannot believe it. If it had been so—if man had invented a method for recording his history—this story would end at this point. But since most scientists do not believe that the Azilian pebbles were actually a form of writing, we will go on to the time when, beyond any dispute, man was recording his own story.

The Azilians were not content with stylizing design. They stylized their frescoes. There are no more splendid animal paintings. Instead, those cave walls ornamented by the Azilians, particularly those in Spain, are covered with pictures conventionalized to an extreme degree. Human figures and animals are both reduced to mere lines. While the lines sometimes make a clear picture, as time passed they became more and more like symbols.

It seems as if we were going forward very

quickly indeed. Time, as man reckons it, was nearing Modern Time. The animals were already

AZILIAN PAINTED PEBBLES. FOUND AT MAS D'AZIL.
(AFTER BREUIL.)

such as are found in Europe today although man has rendered some of them extinct. The final retreat of the glaciers was probably under twenty thousand years ago, so we have but a few thousand years left from man's first million. On one continent

Historic Time was really within sight as we shall soon find out.

Meanwhile in modernizing Europe one race of men followed another and we can tell their cultures but hardly their bones apart. The next people to leave records of their existence centered their evidence around that part of Europe which was near the Mediterranean. These people were flint workers using very small cores. From these the flints struck off were smaller still and were finished so that they appear in almost geometric forms. That is, their shapes are bounded by lines forming regular curves, lines, and angles. So tiny are these implements that they are spoken of as microliths. Compared with the four-inch harpoons of the Magdalenians they are small, for an inch would cover the size of the average implement. Many of these are finished along one edge only but a few were made with both margins chipped.

Since the climate of Europe was nearing its present state, it is not strange that the station where these points were found was an open air camp. It was discovered in the park of an old estate in the Aisne district of France by a French judge whose hobby was prehistoric archaeology. From Tardenoise, the name of the village near the estate, those flints and others found later were called Tardenoisian.

The fact that bone implements are rare after the Magdalenian times and that the few are not well made is not so strange. The hand quickly looses it cunning without practice and the great source material—the reindeer—had disappeared from central and southern Europe. Deer abounded but, as we said, they are more difficult to hunt and so never furnished as much working material.

It is of course the animal bones found with the various types of weapons which tell us what spoils of the hunt furnished the most food during the different periods. So we learn that the Azilians and Tardenoisians ate venison and pork. This latter was supplied by the fierce wild boar of Europe which is still hunted on the great game preserves. In connection with this hunting and on the evidence of fossilized bones we find an interesting item of information. Sometime—perhaps as early as Azilian times, perhaps a little later than Tardenoisian—the prehistoric hunters tamed the ancestors of our dogs. Now to domesticate an animal is a long step toward becoming a modern man. The effort involved is realized by those who have educated puppies, even granting the necessary difference in brutality then and now. Undoubtedly dogs were of use in hunting but when hunting was unsuccessful they must have added an item of food themselves.

It does seem strange that during the countless thousands of years in which the horse was plentiful and was used for food it was never domesticated. Yet its absence after the tundras disappeared is proof that this did not happen. Man had actually entered Historic Time—our little short centuries—before he broke the wild horse to his service. The picture of primitive man as a bare-back rider must remain a myth.

Before Historic Time men of various cultures had established themselves in different parts of the world. The next to stand in the chain of progress from past to present lived in a part of Europe which had been uninhabitable for thousands of years. This was the Scandinavian peninsula where the glaciers lingered many centuries after they had left the rest of Europe. Only a little while after the glaciers left the greater part of it clear—perhaps seven or eight thousand years before Historic Time began—men were living there.

Whether they lived on the shores of a great lake, partly fed by melting glaciers, whether some lived on islands in that lake, or whether some even lived on crude rafts lashed together we are not sure. However they lived, it was the lake which gave us knowledge of their existence. When Modern Time really came and the lake was no longer fed by the melting glaciers, it dried into a great peat bog which preserved in its depths the records of this period of Pleistocene Scandinavia.

In this great bog, Maglemose (Great Swamp), in Denmark, implements were unearthed in 1900. Between that date and 1917 two more stations were found. The tools found in the three certainly suggest that the people who made them had something in common with the Azilians and Tardenoisians. There are microliths very like those made by the Tardenoisians, while some of the flint and bone implements suggest Azilian influence. Picks and knives were made of flint and axes were both of flint and horn. Whatever the blade, the ax helves were of deerhorn. One new implement is a bone fish-hook which might be invented by a people living so close to a great lake. We have all learned that "necessity is the mother of invention" and a spear is difficult fishing apparatus, though a bow and arrow (if some of the smaller points *are* arrow-points) is a better one.

Another new weapon was a combination of bone and flint. This was a lance point made of bone. The bone was grooved along the edge and into this groove small flints were fitted and held there, we are fairly sure, by rosin.

These people like their predecessors in southern Europe certainly domesticated the dog. Probably for the same reasons since the fossil bones show that the red deer, the wild boar, and the bison formed the main food source. To these were also

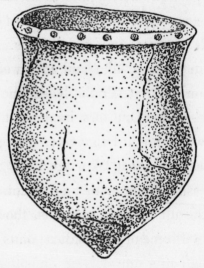

EARLY POTTERY VESSEL WITH POINTED BASE. FOUND IN DENMARK.

added the roe deer, seal, and elk. These northern people added shellfish and fish to their diet more sparingly than we might have thought.

It was left to a race living much later—as man reckons lateness—in this same epoch to make a great addition to human culture. This was the making of pottery. Pieces of this were first found in the domestic refuse heaps or "kitchen middens" left by prehistoric inhabitants of Denmark. All the early pieces are those of jars with conical bottoms. Why the jars were made in this curious form which makes it impossible for them to stand upright, it is difficult to guess. Probably the jars rested in depressions scooped out of earth or sand and were used as storage jars for roots, berries, and acorns against the hard times of winter. Certainly they were a great improvement on cave corners and when a people chose a lake shore or small islands in a lake for dwelling purposes, caves were not available. Though this introduction of pottery is later than the flint and bone industry, we are sure that it is not modern. The weapons found with the jars were hafted in pine. Oak, the herald of modern climate, was not yet available.

20

A CHANGING WORLD

WHEN the oak and other deciduous (leaf-shedding) trees which can only live with sun and warmth for part of the year advanced into the Scandinavian peninsula, Modern Time had really arrived. Just before this happened one of the last changes in geography was made. The English Channel was carved out at the very end of the Pleistocene and the physical geography of the world was brought up to modern standards.

A general change in man's way of living coincided with the world's adjustment to its present geographic conditions. This was partly accident and partly the result of permanent conditions over vast stretches of land. As the climate had become milder men had increased in numbers, first in the security of caves, then in the open camps. More people meant that the work of living could be divided since there were more helping hands. Division of work meant increased needs, for the hauler of wood could not hunt and the hunter had no time for hauling wood. The potter would make his pots but had no time to keep his household implements in shape, while the flint worker had less time for ceramics.

With the increase in population there was more meeting (both friendly and unfriendly) among people. So the cultures—man's entire way of life— grew more uniform. What happened in one part of Europe happened in another part only a little time later. So we can speak of "culture" and not "cultures"—for though there are slight individual differences there is a general distribution of the main type.

Since almost all the implements made for the next few thousand years are of polished stone, the French, who first named this era, called it the Neolithic—the Age of Polished Stone. This does not mean that stone implements and ornaments had not been polished before. They had. But polishing had never before been a part of manufacture. All the flint work of the Neolithic Age is not polished. A number of implements—among them hammer-stones and anvils—continued to be rough. On the whole, however, tools and weapons were made from neatly struck flakes, carefully chipped, ground, and polished.

This was not done at once. During the first part of the four thousand years which made up the Neo-lithic period, tools were much like those found in the Maglemose culture. Indeed that stage, together with the Azilian and Tardenoisian, form three steps between methods of the Old Stone Age and the New or Neolithic Period. In summing up the last steps leading so easily to the new cultures it may be said that as flint-working methods again improved and as pottery slowly developed art degenerated. The great murals of the Old Stone Age were not repeated. It was only on the edge of Historic Time and on a different continent that mural art again became noteworthy.

As the centuries passed, the cruder methods of flint working disappeared and new techniques producing finely finished implements were devised. Two of these techniques were pecking and grinding. In the first the material selected for manufacturing purposes (and it was not always flint) was literally pecked with a stone tool until the surfaces so treated were worn to the desired shape. In grinding, one stone was patiently rubbed along another until the entire surface was ground into shape. One stone might even be sawed through with another, the "saw" being drawn back and forth along the same lines until the worked stone was cut into shape. Frequently two methods might be used in making and finishing an implement. So axes, adzes, and chisels were made from neatly chipped cores and then finished by grinding and polishing. Knives, daggers, and scrapers were made from flakes chipped all over on both faces. Axes, hammers, and like tools were made from rock by picking and grinding. The spear points which were made like the knives were long flakes nearly nine inches in length and all the tools had grown larger as they had grown better made. Very late in the period the use of drills came in. These were, in Europe at least, largely made of flint and were solid, boring a hole through an implement slowly but successfully.

Curiously enough, the oustanding interest in the Neolithic Period is not the workmanship which gave it its name. The Neolithic is the period when man established the foundations of modern living conditions. In earlier times all men were nomadic hunters, living the kind of lives that such an occupation and changing climatic conditions enforced. In the Neolithic, under permanent conditions of geography and climate, men became dwellers at fixed points because they turned farmers.

With more human beings to divide the work and with the development of different needs, the common necessity became food. When the discovery was gradually made that certain animals could be kept as the dog was—where man willed—and that certain grains could be made to grow in places

242

where men found it convenient to gather them, modern civilization was begun. Of course this did not happen quickly. Four or five thousand years were needed for the first stages. Even when man had had so many hundreds of thousands of years behind him he had not the ability for quick adjustment and progress which man living in Historic Time has developed. At the end of many centuries domesticated animals were little more than wild animals kept in subjection by men and grains still showed that they had recently chosen their own fields.

Farmers have fixed dwellings. About one home grow the homes of other families all using near-by fields and pasturage. Moreover there was still need for defense. The time was not peaceful; the conditions Caesar described were not so unlike these centuries. At last people began to feel the need for regulating the use of pastures and the division of labor. Family control is as old as the family but now came the organization of fixed dwelling. Government advanced a step.

Dwellings of various kinds suited to different needs were constructed. While they greatly improved during the centuries of the Neolithic Period, all were a variety of hut. The most primitive type was a pit dwelling which is little more than a hole in the ground with a roof over it. At the end of this Age of Polished Stone, huts had become such livable places as the Pile-Dwellers or Lake-Dwellers built in Switzerland. These huts were made of rough logs but they were houses with doors and an open space under the eaves through which the smoke escaped. Every house, private or communal, had a hearth. These Lake-Dwellers were among the most advanced people of the Neolithic Period, not merely because they built the best huts but because they carried cattle raising to a point only attained by great thought and co-operation.

Cattle were not the only domestic animals. As cultivated land—even crudely cultivated land tended by stone-bladed hoes and pointed sticks— increased, it became easier for man to find his food animals close at hand. Sheep, goats, and pigs were added to cattle and the dog. Not that man ceased hunting. That certainly remained an important occupation for many centuries. When actual need ceased, habit and pleasure persisted in retaining the hunt. We still celebrate, with considerable pomp, man's oldest occupation.

During the time when most implements were still stone, man—or woman—discovered that a certain plant could be made into thread. Flax was spun and woven by the Lake-Dwellers. Wool also they learned to use. Probably twisting, netting, and knitting preceded weaving. But the Neolithic saw looms established with weights made of clay and stone. Judging by some of the very late cave paintings which belong to the early part of this period women were then wearing short skirts fitting at the waist.

Personal ornaments were still made of polished bone, but polished stone was also used and shell had its place. One of the most curious discoveries was that of the Neolithic workshop which had specialized in bracelets. This was at Montcombroux in France and more than three thousand fragments of partly finished bracelets were found with the tools used in their manufacture.

It is not so strange that one workshop should have specialized in this form of ornament. Trade is almost as old as man and, as conditions of travel improved, exchange and barter were carried out over wide areas. By late Neolithic times there were regular routes throughout Europe—some across mountains, some between waterways. But the real trade routes are part of the succeeding ages.

Some of the old customs still clung and among them is ceremonial burial. Like almost everything else it changed as the Neolithic Period grew older. During the early part, bodies were buried much as they had been in the time of unpolished stone. Then caves, no longer needed for dwellings, were turned into tombs and stones often closed the entrances as they did in the Neolithic burials at Cro-Magnon. Next artificial burial caves were made and stones protected the dead. Stone cists (five stones ar-

ranged box-fashion) had their period of use before the Neolithic people turned to their use of
mounds, barrows, and the erection of marking
stones of large proportions. The dolmens belong to
the stones marking graves—individual or multiple.

The huge alignments of separate menhirs (long
stones set on end) probably have religious signifi-
cance but no connection with burials. Stonehenge
is one of the best known alignments of menhirs in
the world. It was probably built only a century or
two before Historic Time began, but it was built by
a people who had worked in western Europe before crossing into England.

Toward the end of the Neolithic Period came an
epoch usually called the Age of Copper because
almost all implements and ornaments of this time
were made from that metal. In Europe it was about
two thousand years before Historic Time began but
the use of copper had begun at least three thousand
years earlier in Egypt. Man's discovery of the means
of working the softer metals was probably acci-
dental. He had known gold for a much longer time

but, although he may have collected the dust which never tarnishes, he had little use for it. Even the nuggets were too soft for use. This, at least, was the European view-point. In Africa, while European men were experimenting with copper, gold played a part in ornament and as one of the commodities of commerce.

Almost simultaneously, we think, the use of copper and tin was discovered in different parts of the world. Probably the first smelting was pure accident. Stones containing copper ore or, in Europe, tin or iron ore were used to build a hearth. The heat melted the ore in the stones and it is easy to imagine the surprise when men found lumps quite different from stone in the ashes. After the first stage of conjecture, experiment must have followed. Possibly some startled man hit at a cooling trickle of metal and saw it flatten under the blow and retain that shape. Since the most primitive stage of metal working today is the hammering of metal into shape, that was undoubtedly the process at the very end of the Age of Polished Stone. The

Age of Copper was the beginning of planned experiment which was so successful that metal tools and weapons, modeled on the old stone implements, were soon used the continent over.

The next step must have been the making of a clay mold covered by embers into which the metal ran. Soon came experiment with another metal. Bronze, a mixture of tin and copper which is harder and better suited for weapons, followed the use of copper alone. Ornaments of elaborate pattern were wrought from it. The arts of weaving and basket making improved greatly. Clothing became elaborate. Agriculture and husbandry developed. Pottery was devised for something more than mere utilitarian purposes and bronze was also used for storage vessels.

There must have been sun-worship during this period. A bronze chariot belonging to the Bronze Age evidently represents the chariot of the sun and pottery was made into votive offerings inscribed with the sun symbol. Indeed the sun symbol had been engraved on a bâton de commandement belonging to the end of the Paleolithic Period.

Art in the form of engraving persisted chiefly in connection with burial stones. Burials themselves changed from the burial of the body with pottery vessels and bronze ornaments and weapons to the disposal of the body by incineration.

These developments occupied only about fifteen hundred years—the tempo of life was evidently quickening. The Iron Age which followed the Bronze was barely under way before Historic Time was at hand in Europe. In Egypt iron began to be used while Europe was in the middle of its Age of Polished Stone. Besides much greater development in all the useful arts, the Iron Age in Europe saw a very real improvement in the development of commerce. Those great adventurers of the north, the Vikings, made their almost incredible journeys while the Bronze Age was at its height. When the Iron Age reached Europe, the great Minoan culture found at Knossos in Crete had ended, Egypt had witnessed the enslavement and exodus of the

Hebrews, Saul had fallen on his sword, and Homer would chant his poems in another hundred years or so. The end of the Iron Age is recorded, practically, by Caesar's comments on the tribes of Gaul. All these events make books in themselves—some of them would make several books. There can be no doubt that Historic Time had come to Europe but it had already come, much earlier, on another continent.

21

CATCHING UP WITH THE CONTINENTS

SO far we have talked almost entirely about Europe, or rather about the southern and western parts of Europe, with only a trip outside here and there. This is because a great deal more is known about the prehistoric archaeology of this part of the world than any other. It has been more carefully studied and for a much longer time than in any other section of the earth. Only lately —as you can see from the dates of some of the discoveries—have archaeologists had the opportunity to study on other continents.

Once or twice we have spoken of new races of men coming from Asia and from Africa. Indeed we nominated Asia as the probable homeland of man. The very recent date when man's second-in-line ancestor was actually found gives us some idea of how little is yet known about Asia. For this there are many reasons. Chief among them is the action Asia took in shutting herself away from the rest of the world for a long period. It is only within the last few years that students have been able to penetrate Asia's hidden history.

Between the Ape-man of Java and Peking Man we have no records. After the time of Peking Man we can only make a brief, general summary of what has, so far, been learned. Flints like those of Mousterian and Aurignacian times are found in southern Asia. Because Asia had no glaciers and so there are no deposits made as these melted, it is not so easy to determine the age of Asiatic flints as exactly as has been done in Europe. In Siberia man's flints, found with mammoth bones, belong to the later periods of the Stone Age. Since the cold-loving fauna lingered longer in Siberia than in Europe these flints may not be so old as similar flints in southern Europe. Their makers may have kept a manner of living and of working flints which had vanished in the south. Stations of the Polished Stone Age stretch from the Ural Mountains to the Amur River and on the coast, near Bering Strait, there are traces of a people who made pottery.

Recent study has also brought to light another fact about a different part of Asia. Western Asia— the part always associated with the Bible and where the Euphrates valley leads into another continent—was probably the spot where man first left behind his nomadic habits and settled himself upon the earth as a cultivator. The reason for thinking this is that the first cultivated grains are natives of this region. A wheat was cultivated in Egypt fifty centuries before Historic Time began and ten centuries later Babylonia and Egypt were both using cultivated barley and millet as well as wheat.

We have few fossil records in Africa owing to the climate and those few are not connected. Rhodesian Man or, as it is sometimes called, the Broken Hill Skull which was found in 1921 has been difficult to place in the line of human development. It had a superficial resemblance to Neandertal Man but when the skull was finally cleaned and measured many differences were found. The palate is enormous, the brow-ridges very pronounced. The head must have been carried erect. The back part of the skull is primitive and the brain capacity small. It seems doubtful that other bone fragments found at the same time belong with the skull. Only two species of animals whose bones were found in the cave with the skull are extinct, but many African animals have survived on that continent when their near kin perished in Europe. So possibly Rhodesian Man may represent a primitive type surviving under mild climatic conditions long after his kind had vanished from the rest of the world. It is possible that so strange a combination of characters may be individual peculiarities. Indeed the only certainty is that Rhodesian Man is a puzzle.

The same is true of two other famous African discoveries. In 1913 the Boskop skull was discovered in the Transvaal. Since then other bones have been found which are believed to belong to

255

the same type of man. At least one scientist is convinced that these remains represent a distinct species and he has assigned them the name *Homo capensis*, Man of the Cape. While the skulls suggest those of modern Bushmen, their owners were far taller and their brains far larger.

Equally problematic is the Oldoway skeleton found in the old German East Africa in 1913. The trouble here is the inability to determine the geologic age. Some scientists follow its discoverer in thinking it a Pleistocene man. Others believe that it is a man of Modern Time, washed into Pleistocene gravels by chance.

The study of flints in Africa has only started, but the results have been interesting in the extreme. Chellean, Acheulian, and Mousterian flints have been found in quantities in northern and western Africa and in parts of the southern section. Lately the work of American scientists in Egypt has made it possible to determine with accuracy the ages of the flints found there and to compare them with those of Europe. We can now say with

256

fair certainty that prehistoric man living in Egypt developed various types of flints several thousand years earlier than man living in Europe, which, of course, seems an added argument for the earliest migrations of man having been from Africa into Europe.

When we get to the ages of metals we are not only on safer ground but we are on historic ground in every sense. Troy, which has proved to be a prehistoric settlement as well as a historic city, possessed copper utensils in 2000 B.C. Cyprus paid tribute to Totmes III somewhere about 1500 B.C. with copper vases included in the reckoning. Seti I and Rameses II could not drive out the Hittites whose iron weapons were far superior to their copper ones. And this, of course, was long after man's record of his own activities was well established.

The Hittites had discovered their iron in Asia Minor, which forms a sort of bridge into western Asia. We began our history of man's first million years in Asia and have come back to it again. During the early part of the Pleistocene the Persian

Gulf was larger and extended farther north and west. Along the shores of this prehistoric sea have been found traces of Stone Age hunters. Their flints are found under the ruins of Babylonian cities. We have already noted that the Neandertals were found just west of Asia Minor proper in Palestine, and that man probably began his agricultural career in the valley of the Euphrates.

Western Asia was in advance of eastern Asia and various cultures have been found represented there. India has yielded evidence of cave and open air dwellings belonging to the various stages of the Stone Age and a crude cave art has been discovered there.

It is possible that man may have used northern Asia or Siberia as a stepping stone to another continent. Certainly implements typical of Mousterian and Aurignacian work have been found there. Near Irkutsk there has been a discovery apparently belonging to the Magdalenian period. Neolithic work, associated with pottery, has been found in Kamchatka.

Finally there are the numberless islands which stretch far from southern Asia into the Pacific Ocean. They have at present a dense and mixed population. Pleistocene flints have been found there, but they are surprisingly few for a land which would have been thought of as a stronghold of Pleistocene life. The islands north of New Guinea seemed hopeful because they contained stone circles, ruined megaliths, and stone implements. But some of the megaliths are considered old, some are still in use, some are being built. The archaeologist has not made progress which a layman can appreciate.

Australia and New Zealand and Tasmania would seem to have been one of the last outposts which primitive man would have reached. Drifting bands would—it seems certain—have arrived there and stopped. Some anthropologists believe that this was so and that the living Australians are remnants of an ancient people. But modern methods of research fail to confirm this. On the other hand they raise new problems of their own which make the rela-

259

tion of the living Australian to prehistoric humanity doubtful.

Who has not heard of Easter Island and imagined that its strange stone figures might be relics of a race vanished before the world was old? Yet native records date them within man's division of Ancient History. Still, native records can hardly be taken with complete belief. The fact remains that here, as on that island continent Australia, primitive man must have existed. These islands, close enough to be reached easily one from another, must have been the final habitable ground reached by prehistoric migrants. Europeans, who have never left undisturbed the primitive simplicity they found, reached these same islands very late indeed. Some are still unspoiled. So far as can be judged from the evidence left undisturbed by the latest European invasion, two early invasions took place. The first was probably that of a people with the hunting habits of late Paleolithic times. The second, later invasion was by a people who probably erected the megaliths. These invaders already had the beginnings of a system of agriculture. Because this last land into which they penetrated was not a land where such a system could be applied, agricultural habits died.

These islands are not so far from the American continents as we might think. Many have believed that America was populated from Polynesia. No one denies that certain cultural traits seem curiously the same. The Pacific coast from Alaska to Costa Rica shows odd instances of shell, bone, and stone manufactures which seem too like those of the Pacific Islands to be mere chance. It is also true that the early inhabitants of Polynesia were magnificent navigators sailing by star and not by compass. Before Europeans had ventured outside their Mediterranean borders, voyagers from the Pacific are said to have visited the Antarctic. Archaeologists tell us that there is no doubt that some of them reached America from time to time and were absorbed into the population already existing there. That they were comparatively few in number is indicated by the fact that neither the physi-

261

cal build nor the language of the Americans seems to have been influenced. Only the cultures profited by new items.

How early—or how late—man was in South America is an unsolved problem. Great antiquity has been claimed and disproved. So far there is little reason to believe that he entered South America much before the Pleistocene had ended. The great sloths lingered on the Southern continent until very late indeed. The mastodons lived almost into a modern world. Man's implements have been found with their fossils which proves only that man was living in South America about thirty thousand years ago. Such a man was *Homo sapiens* and capable of being a migrant. Such a date of entrance would have given more than enough time for the development and decay of the empire which the Spaniards found. The height of the culture was past, the empire disintegrating when they came. The first thousand years of the Christian era saw the Maya empire at its highest point. That was far too late to fall within man's first million years.

We still have to explain how the first people entered South America if we do not believe that migration from the Pacific was the real source. Curiously enough, we believe—as evidence now stands —that both the Americas were entered from the north. The west coast of North America and, by some strange chance, the Rocky Mountains were not under the pall of ice which stretched as far south as Iowa and New York in the last part of the Ice Age when we believe the first Americans arrived. So they traveled toward the south along the coast, adapting themselves to different climates as they went. Since we believe that people have been in South America for less than forty thousand years, they must have adapted themselves very rapidly to changes in climate. It ordinarily takes a much longer period than this for a people to survive the change from an arctic to a tropical climate.

This theory makes the American Indian also an immigrant from Asia. Since the Indian's physical make-up strongly suggests relationship with the

Mongols, this does not seem very farfetched. The record of fossil man in America is not a long one. The first discovery was made in 1844 and one of the most interesting—the so-called Folsom discovery—only about fifteen years ago. This last consisted of arrow points of curious manufacture undoubtedly associated with extinct bison. Indeed it became evident that the bison had been driven over a low bluff above a lake and slaughtered as ancient man on all continents has made his meat kills. The arrow points are Neolithic (polished stone) in general style, hollowed in the middle of each side, possibly for attachment to the shaft, and edged by the removal of innumerable tiny flakes.

Other finds of arrows with mammoth bones have been made and also with other extinct animals. Of over one hundred and sixty finds so far recorded a little over seventy have been with extinct animals but only sixty have had human fossils. All of these are the remains of *Homo sapiens*. Of course, once man had learned to adapt the world to his needs, he had less physical need to change his body to adapt himself to the world. *Homo sapiens* may be older than we think but if so there is no proof. The skeletons found in North America could not be distinguished from those of living Indians. None of the finds dates before the advance of glaciers on this continent. Some, indeed almost all, are clearly later than a time when glaciers retreated —a time geologists place about thirty thousand years ago.

How did man get to America? Probably by way of Bering Strait. During a large part of the Pleistocene, Bering Strait was open. During another part, owing to the retreat of the sea as the ice failed to liberate moisture, the strait was dry land. At the time man is believed to have come it was open. Islands are near each other. The distance would be little more than fifty miles from shore to shore. It would not have been a difficult trip.

To strengthen this hypothesis, the earliest cultures in America seem to be those of the west. Man seems to have spread toward the Atlantic. These cultures are those of a people of Neolithic habits—

a state which the American Indian retained. They were hunters.

Agriculture originated in America in the central portion. We know this because our Indian corn, or maize as it is often called, must have been cultivated from a stock which grew in Mexico and Guatemala. Metal working and pottery accompanied the cultivation of corn and spread, as that did, both southward and northward.

In North America perhaps the outstanding achievement of the people was the creation of the pueblo. We have heard so much of this from an architectural standpoint that it is hardly necessary to comment on it.

We have seen man on all the continents. We have read his records as geologist, paleontologist, archaeologist, and anatomist have read them. We have found that man in all his million years was a hunter, fighter, manufacturer, and adventurer. Indeed we have realized, probably with surprise, that our early ancestors were far more adventurous explorers than their descendants. In his first mil-

CATCHING UP WITH THE CONTINENTS

lion years man discovered all the continents. His descendants, living in Historic Time, have added but two spots on the map which were utterly unknown to their prehistoric ancestors. Those two spots are the poles.

Besides this great sweep of exploration, prehistoric man began the development of agriculture. The complex social organization which we today find hard to adjust was begun more than a million years ago. Manufactures of various kinds date their origin long before Historic Time and on what he taught himself in those first million of uncounted years man, who counts the centuries, has based his modern civilization.

BIBLIOGRAPHY

BLACK, DAVIDSON
  Sinanthropus Pekinensis: A further note, etc. *Proceedings, 4th Pacific Science Congress*, 1929, Vol. III, pp. 105-112. 1929.
BLACK, TEILHARD DE CHARDIN ET AL.
  Fossil Man in China. Geological Memoirs, Geological Survey of China, Series A, No. 11. 1933.
BROWN, F. MARTIN
  America's Yesterdays. 8vo., J. B. Lippincott, Philadelphia. 1938.
CAPITAN, LOUIS
  La Préhistoire. 12mo., Payot & Cie., Paris. 1922.
McCURDY, GEORGE GRANT
  Human Origins—A Manual of Prehistory. 2 vols. 8vo. D. Appleton, New York. 1924.
McGREGOR, J. HOWARD
  Human Origins and Early Man. In "General Anthropology," edited by Franz Boas, pp. 24-94. D. C. Heath and Co., Boston. 1938.
NELSON, NELS C.
  Geological Premises. Ibid, pp. 7-16. 1938.

  Prehistoric Archaeology. Ibid, pp. 146-237.

PEAKE, H. J. AND FLEUR, HERBERT JOHN
   The Corridors of Time—Vol. I—Apes and Men;
   Vol. II—Hunters and Artists. Clarendon Press,
   Oxford. 1927.

OBERMAIER, HUGO
   Fossil Man in Spain. 8vo., Hispanic Society of
   America. 1924.

OSBORN, HENRY FAIRFIELD
   The Hall of the Age of Man. Revised by William
   K. Gregory and George Pinkley. Guide Leaflet,
   American Museum of Natural History, No. 52.
   1938.

PAGET, SIR RICHARD A. S.
   The Origin of Speech—A Hypothesis. *Proceedings,
   Royal Society,* Series A, Vol. 119, pp. 157-172.
   1928.

   Human Speech. *Nature,* February 26, 1929.

STEVENS, FRANK
   Stonehenge Today and Yesterday. (Official Guide)
   8vo., London. 1938.

WEIDENREICH, FRANZ
   The Sinanthropus Population of Choukoutien (Lo-
   cality 1) with a Preliminary Report of New Discoveries. *Bulletin, Geological Society of China,* Vol.
   14, pp. 427-468. 1935.

   The Forerunners of Sinanthropus Pekinensis. *Bul-*

270

letin, Geological Society of China, Vol. 14, pp. 137-144. 1935.

Six Lectures on Sinanthropus Pekinensis and Related Problems. *Bulletin, Geological Society of China,* Vol. 19, pp. 1-110. 1939.

Each of these titles has either a bibliography or references in footnotes. These make an extensive list of important papers on prehistoric archaeology.

INDEX

Acheulian, 131-138, 148, 170

Africa, 68, 72, 100, 104, 116, 119, 136, 154, 155, 160, 163, 254, 255, 256

America, 261
North, 263-265
South, 262-263

Agriculture, 243, 244, 254, 258, 261, 266

Anatomy, 9-11

Anvil, 144, 213

Ape, 11, 22, 24, 27, 28, 32, 36
relation to man, 32
See Primates.

Ape-man, 38-40, 42, 43, 46, 47, 49, 50, 72, 253

Art, 181, 191, 193, 221, 249
See Cave painting, Sculpture.

Asia, 35, 38, 44, 72, 75, 76, 82, 119, 122, 155, 157, 163, 196, 226, 253, 254, 258

Aurignacian, 169, 170, 173, 174, 181-196, 253, 259
See Cro-Magnon.

Australia, 259, 260

Azilian, 226-230, 235

Backbone, 18

Basket-making, 249

Bâton de commandement, 179, 214, 249

Bering Strait, 254, 265

Bison, 111, 113, 150, 186, 187, 222

Boar, wild, 113, 232

Brain, 17, 18, 22, 40, 50, 63, 85, 86

Brain cast, 40

Bronze Age, 249, 250

Burial, 146, 147, 164, 182, 209, 246, 247, 250

Burin. *See* Point.

Camp, 87, 103, 106, 108, 132, 138, 197, 205, 231, 239

Capsian, 156

Cattle, 88, 113, 150, 186

Caves, 128
Altamira, 185, 187, 189, 222

273

Caves (Cont.)
  Aurignac, 169
  Chapelle-aux-Saints, 147, 149
  Cro-Magnon, 162
  Font de Gaume, 183, 222
  Grotte des Enfants, 168
  Grottes de Grimaldi, 157
  Mas d'Azil, 215, 226
  Moustier, Le, 139, 147, 209
  Pindal, 182
  Three Brothers, 215, 217
Cave painting, 183-193, 216, 217, 222-224, 240
  method of dating, 190, 191
Chellean, 111, 112
Chelles, 106
Cleaver, 100, 106, 107, 108, 135, 138, 143
Clothing, 249
  See Skins.
Copper Age, 247-249
Coup de poing. See Cleaver.
Cro-Magnons, 159, 161-165, 167, 168, 181, 191, 196, 208, 246
Culture, 91, 92, 144, 145, 173, 239

Deer, 45, 61, 111, 113, 150, 225, 232, 236
Dog, 233, 235
Dolmen, 247

Domestic animals, 233, 242, 243, 244, 245
Dryopithecus, 27

Egypt, 256, 257
Elephant, 45, 88, 111, 150, 216, 220, 225, 253
English Channel, 88, 238
Eoanthropus. *See* Piltdown Man.
Eoliths, 73, 74, 97
Eskimo, 195, 206
Eurasia, 87
Europe, 66, 67, 68, 69, 71, 72, 82, 116, 196, 252

Feet, 16
Fire, 50, 58, 59, 62, 138, 175, 198
Flints, 90, 91, 135, 231
  abandoned, 210
  Acheulian, 131-135, 148, 170, 256
  Aurignacian, 170, 173-180
  Azilian, 227
  Chellean, 95, 106-109, 132, 135, 256
  core, 95
  face, 95
  flake, 95
  Magdalenian, 209-210
  manufacture, 92-93, 95

Flints (Cont.)
  Mousterian, 131, 134, 141,
    143, 144, 148, 156, 170,
    256
  Neolithic, 240
  Nodule, 95
  Peking Man's, 60
  Pre-Chellean, 99-101, 132
  Solutrean, 199-203
Fish-hook, 235
Food, 50, 62, 191, 205, 220,
    232, 236, 242, 243
Fossil, 5, 6, 33

Geological periods, 3
Glacial periods:
  First, 66-72
  Second, 105
  Third, 118, 119
  Fourth, 153, 154
Glaciers, 67, 68, 72, 73, 90,
    100, 105, 138, 139, 207,
    225, 234
  cause of, 68, 71
Government, 243
Great Ice Age, 4
Grimaldi race, 157-160, 163

Hammer-stone, 94, 95, 106,
    144, 174, 213, 227
Hand-ax. *See* Cleaver.
Harpoon, 213, 214, 228, 235
Head, upright position, 18, 85

Heidelberg Man, 112-117
Himalayas, 36, 45
Homo sapiens, 37, 154, 167,
    173, 195, 208, 226, 264
Horse, 111, 113, 204, 216,
    220, 225, 226, 233
Hunting, 49, 63, 87, 88, 103,
    153, 183, 205, 216-218
Huts, 63, 244
Hyena, 45, 88, 108, 111, 150

India, 27, 61
Indian, American, 263, 264
Interglacial Period:
  First, 72, 73, 75-79, 90, 91,
    104
  Second, 105, 111
  Third, 119
  Fourth, 154, 191, 207, 225,
    265
Iron Age, 250

Java, 38, 39, 44, 75

Knife, 107, 173, 174, 175,
    191, 199, 235, 241
  See Scraper.
Krapina, 148, 149

Lake Dwelling, 244
Lance, 176, 179, 200, 213,
    235
  See Spear.
Land-bridge, 68, 69, 104, 155

Magdalenians, 208-226, 258
Magic, 182, 216-220
Maglemose, 234
Mammoth. *See* Elephant.
Man:
  ancestral form, 10, 11, 12, 35, 37
  early, 72, 74, 75, 82
  origin, 33-36
  See Ape Man, Cro-Magnon, Grimaldi, Heidelberg, *Homo sapiens*, Mousterian, Neandertal, Oldoway, Peking, Piltdown, Rhodesian
Mauer, 116
Menhirs, 247
Migrations:
  animal, 68, 105, 153, 155
  human, 46, 75, 76, 79, 155, 157, 207
"Missing Link," 38
Mousterian, 140, 148, 149, 150, 153, 191, 253
Murals. *See* Cave painting.
Muscles, 18

Neandertal, 119-127, 131, 139, 144, 151, 156, 192, 255
Neolithic, 169, 170, 239-248, 254, 264
New Stone Age. *See* Neolithic.
Notharctus, 11, 12, 13

Ochre, 149, 168, 189
Old Stone Age, 91, 240
  See Acheulian, Aurignacian, Chellean, Magdalenian, Mousterian, Pre-Chellean
Oldoway Man, 256
Ornaments, 158, 169, 181, 245, 246, 249

Pacific
  Islands, 259, 260, 261
  Ocean, 44, 259, 261
Pebbles, painted, 228-230
Peking Man, 52-55, 57, 61-64, 72, 74, 75, 81, 82, 128
Piltdown Man, 75, 79-82, 83, 85, 86, 116, 159
Pleistocene, 4, 6, 22
Pliocene, 4, 72
Pliopithecus, 24, 27
Point, 174, 176, 199, 200, 201, 241
Pottery, 236, 237
Pre-Chellean, 96-107
  lack of people, 103
Pressure chipping, 95
Primates, 22, 34, 35, 36
  See Ape.
Propliopithecus, 23, 24

Reconstruction, 55-57, 82
Reindeer, 176, 198, 205, 206,

Reindeer (Cont.)
207, 217, 220, 221, 225, 232

Rhinoceros, 61, 88, 113, 150
Rhodesian Man, 255
Rock shelters, 138, 146

Scandinavia, 234, 238
Scraper, 97, 100, 101, 107, 108, 141, 143, 173, 174, 199, 241
See Knife.
Sculpture, 192, 193, 203, 204, 215-217
Sinanthropus. *See* Peking Man.
Skins, used for clothing, 150, 179, 213
Social life, 129, 130, 163, 242
Solutré, 198, 205
Solutreans, 195-208
Spear, 144, 153, 176, 211, 215, 217, 235
thrower, 211, 215, 217
See Harpoon, Lance.

Speech, 40, 128-129
Stone Age, 194, 206, 253, 258

Tardenoisian, 231-233, 235
Teeth, 10
pattern, 24, 27, 28, 31
Terraces, river, 73, 104
Thumb, 16
Time
ancient, 4, 5, 6, 35
historic, 7, 234, 240, 251, 252
modern, 234, 238
recent, 6, 7
Tool. *See* Flints.
Trade route, 246
Tree dwelling, 12, 15

Vikings, 250

Weaving, 249
Weapons. *See* Flints.
Wood, use of, 143, 144, 220

277

THE APE-MAN OF JAVA

PILTDOWN MAN